NEVER, NEVER, HARDLY EVER

A Mother-Daughter Story of Antiques and Antics

KELLY MCKENZIE

Never, Never, Hardly Ever:
A Mother-Daughter Story of Antiques and Antics

Published by Tolmie Press
Burnaby, BC

Names: McKenzie, Kelly, author.

Title: Never, never, hardly ever : a mother-daughter story of antiques and antics / Kelly McKenzie.

Description: Burnaby, BC : Tolmie Press, [2024]

Identifiers: ISBN: 978-1-7382395-0-4 (paperback) | 978-1-7382395-2-8 (kindle)

Subjects: LCSH: McKenzie, Kelly--Friends and associates. | Antiques business. | Antique dealers--Biography. | Mothers and daughters. | Antiques--Asia. | Art objects, Asian. | Asia--Collectibles. | Selling--Collectibles. | Friendship. | Coming of age--Biography. | LCGFT: Autobiography. | BISAC: BIOGRAPHY & AUTOBIOGRAPHY / Memoirs.

Classification: LCC: CT310.M34 M34 2024 | DDC: 971.4/05092--dc23

Cover design by Amanda Miller.
Interior design by Asya Blue.

Disclaimer: I have tried to recreate events, locales and conversations from my memories of them. In order to maintain their anonymity, in some instances I have changed the names of individuals and places, and I may have changed some identifying characteristics and details such as physical properties, occupations and places of residence.

QUANTITY PURCHASES: Schools, companies, professional groups, clubs, and other organizations may qualify for special terms when ordering quantities of this title. For information, email kmckenzie13@gmail.com.

TOLMIE
PRESS

To Francine, my treasured fellow quirk magnet. Thank you, Mom, for the opportunity to experience our unique decade of FROG antics and for nudging me to share them with the world.

To Meems, my best friend for over 45 years. Oh, the stories we could tell.

Author's Note

If Frankie opened her Asian antique store today, she would have given it a different name. However, she opened her shop in the late '70s. "Frankie Robinson Oriental Gallery" was of its time. As were her bachelor and master's degrees in Oriental Art History. I've chosen to use the word "Asian" in place of "Oriental" for everything else.

Kelly McKenzie

CHAPTER 1

Ceiling the Deal

A t this rate, my mother would be sporting a neck brace by the end of the day. She'd been fixated on the showroom's ceiling for the past half hour, adamant that a barely visible, gravy-colored smudge was a harbinger of outright structural collapse.

I couldn't be more delighted.

I'd been dreading my remaining three and a half months as the summer employee at Frankie Robinson Oriental Gallery (FROG), after only two weeks on the job. It was as if everyone at Mom's namesake shop possessed a prized golden ticket to a foreign world but me. My mother and her customers shared endlessly insightful conversations while I floundered about like a dullard, useless and bored.

But today's incessant fixation was something different altogether. I loved that the more I ignored my mother, the better it got. She'd now moved on to frenetic hand-flapping.

"It's really quite alarming, Kelly. Do come and look. *Please*," Mom implored, yet again.

Time to placate the old gal, if only to save her poor neck. I kicked back my office chair and ambled into the showroom with all the curiosity of a sated cow.

Sweet Jesus.

My supercilious attitude shattered like a porcelain Ming vase. Not only had the mark mushroomed in size, but also we now had several ominously damp and distended ceiling panels in the mix. I struggled to adopt a reassuring tone.

"We may require some help here, Mom."

"That's what I've been saying all along, Kelly. *Christ.*"

She flew into the tiny back office to alert the landlord, leaving me suitably chastened. At any moment, a torrent of filthy water, soggy construction materials and ceiling panels could indeed come crashing down upon this expensive and carefully hand-picked inventory. However, as I pondered potential umbrella and tarp options, I smiled. I'd forgotten that, as with me, my mother adopted a British accent when stressed.

"I do not need the landlord to return my call, Susan. I require someone who understands plumbing. The shop's ceiling is jiggling like Jell-o. Pardon? J-E-L-L-O. No, I assure you, I am *not* over-reacting. Do stop prattling on, woman, and send me a plumber!"

I was more than a little impressed.

"I'm putting you on notice, Susan. Should that ceiling cave in, I will sue. Not only for loss of business, but also for the full replacement of my inventory." Her clipped tones slid into an ominous hiss. "Toss in the additional repair costs and lost wages, and your boss will be slammed with a bill in the hundreds of thousands of dollars."

The dispatched plumber swept into the shop like magic and confirmed the worst.

"You've got yourselves one hell of a leak, ladies. I've shut off the water but you've got to gut the place. Now."

Excuse me? Now? The timing could not be worse. We spent all of yesterday unpacking a mammoth shipment. It was virtually impossible to move an inch in any direction without fearing for one's safety. Dozens of antique *tansu* were buried beneath piles of antique kimonos, *obis*, temple scrolls, porcelain vases, decorative plates and figurines. But that wasn't all. No. We also had a wealth of antique Chinese wooden chairs, cabinets and tables nestled among several life-size contemporary Thai bronze geese, rabbits and cranes. Honestly, the staggering volume had me not only seriously questioning Mom's purchasing prowess, but also wondering whether the rental of a small warehouse was required.

Today and tomorrow were supposed to be about somehow restoring order to the shop, not gutting it. What's worse, I was a shamefully hungover 26-year-old and my mother was an admittedly out-of-shape 61-year-old. The concept of the pair of us efficiently schlepping the lot out in a timely fashion, to God only knew where, was truly beyond the pale.

Mom shot a final look at the ceiling before nodding.

"Right. We'll gut the damn place. But how? I doubt we could organize a moving van, let alone any professional storage outfit at this short notice." My mother raked her fingers through her shoulder-length hair before slowly smiling. "How about next door?"

I liked it. The adjoining travel agency could work, barring mutual leakage issues. Their space, while even smaller than Mom's, was virtually vacant except for the pair of desks and a few client chairs. But then I considered the owner. A trim, fastidious woman in her mid-60s, Fiona might not welcome an invasion of her pristine workplace. However, Mom thought differently.

"Nonsense. Fiona's a professional. She'll understand we can't just leave everything outside. It could rain."

My mother and the tradesman beetled off for yet another flood consult, leaving the storage inquiry to me. Thankfully, Fiona was alone. I chose my words carefully.

"Good morning, Fiona. I'm delighted your ceiling is healthy. Ours isn't. We've got a bit of a leakage issue and the plumber is insisting that we clear everything out." I deliberately slowed down my pacing, in an effort to appear less needy. "Mom is wondering if we could possibly stash the bulk of our inventory here until he sorts out the problem."

It landed as the confession of a naughty child. The travel agent smiled and swung her arms wide.

"By all means, dear, bring over your bits and bobs. You're welcome to use Bill's desk, too. He's not coming in today."

"Bits and bobs?" Fiona obviously hadn't popped into Mom's depository of late. I shot out before she could have a rethink, only to find the plumber babbling about the need for additional backup. However, my boss was no longer listening. She'd moved on to efficient triaging.

"Right. Let's begin by stuffing as much as we can into the built-ins."

We managed to stash about a quarter of the smaller items into the row of low cabinets before running out of space. It was time to invade Fiona's.

Our efforts weren't pretty. Both of us were dripping with sweat within minutes. However, Mom quickly grasped the need to keep Fiona onside. Once we crossed her threshold, all bickering ceased. Our movements became balletic and synchronized. We efficiently stacked, sorted and placed until we ran out of room and were slammed with the inevitable: encroaching upon Fiona's desk.

As I'd feared, the travel agent's placid mien shattered like fine crystal. She'd tolerated the incessant chiming of her security doormat and the burgeoning wall of stacked chests surprisingly well, but this infringement upon her personal space was too much. The frazzled woman lost her ability to speak; a condition I dearly hoped was short-lived.

My heart went out to the poor soul. In just under two and a half hours, we'd effectively shut down her business. My toes bunched painfully as Fiona's spasmodic headshakes confirmed the absence of an alarm system. We were duty bound to remain until the plumber assured us that we could begin moving everything back. Who knew how long that would take?

I slipped cautiously onto the floor. Blinking myopically in the dim light, I could just make out Fiona slumped at her desk and my exhausted mother wedged between a life-sized, bead-encrusted Thai Buddha and two gigantic bronze cranes. The air grew thick and I felt myself drifting off when Mom suddenly cleared her throat.

"Right. We could do with some hot drinks and comfort food. Kelly, you're closest to the door. Pop down to The Granville Diner for tea and an assortment of baked goodies, would you please?"

Bless her. Anything to escape this stuffy coffin-like place. As I dug out my purse and carefully inched my way toward the door, my mother's cheery falsetto rocketed about the room.

"What's your most popular beach destination, Fiona? This little adventure has me frankly yearning to escape."

Full marks to Frankie. Pure distraction was the only option now. When I returned, she was still at it.

"Kelly, Fiona really is a wealth of information. She was telling me about a beach randomly plunked in the middle of a Spanish meadow! It sounds marvelous. We should go."

Yes, please. Now perhaps.

I stole a quick peek at Fiona. She'd not only recovered her

voice and gained some color in her cheeks, but also somehow managed to eke out a little room for marching in place. Things were looking up.

No one spoke for several minutes as we tucked into the refreshments.

"Here's to you, Fiona! Thank you." Mom whipped her Styrofoam cup skyward and winked at me, secretly confirming my suspicions that the travel agency would be overflowing with floral bouquets of gratitude come morning.

"And, Kelly, I'm truly grateful for your help, also. I couldn't have coped without you."

True. Without me she'd still be hard at it. I saluted her in return. Mom and I could be very proud of what we achieved in such a short period of time. Yes, today's unpredictability was positively refreshing.

I tore into my chocolate chip scone and experienced an epiphany of sorts. Since I was committed to working alongside my mother for the rest of the summer, I might as well try and enjoy it. This shouldn't be too hard; my attitude just needed some tweaking.

What I couldn't possibly comprehend was just how cataclysmic that tweaking would be.

.

CHAPTER 2

Who Got Me Into This?

These 40 years later, I can't actually remember how I ended up working at FROG. However, Mom's diaries back up her assertion that I toddled into the shop one random afternoon and asked to work there for the summer. That's quite possible. I did need tuition money. Having just resigned from a four-year spell as the Senior Citizens' trip coordinator at my brother-in-law's charter bus company, I was heading back to university to become a high school drama teacher. Was this new profession a true calling? Absolutely not. It was all about shutting down my father's endless entreaties to "make proper use of that theater degree." I was 26.

However it happened, Mom said the timing was perfect. She'd worked alone for the past seven years and now, at 61, was ready for quality backup. Who could she trust more than one of her three darling children? We both agreed that there wasn't a hope in hell that my sister or brother would have volunteered, though. Then 29 and 32, Wendy and Mike were married with young children and happily employed elsewhere. That left me, single, jobless and broke, as the lone candidate.

You really had to admire my mother's willingness to hire me at all considering our previous experience. As her slide projectionist some eight years earlier, I delighted in playing the silly ass. Hovering over a projector at the back of the darkened university lecture hall where only she could see me, I did everything possible to throw her off stride in front of her attentive summer school students. She should have fired me on the spot.

While FROG had seen some folks fill in for a few days when Frankie was traveling, I'd be the first serious hire. How did our chances look for surviving the full four months?

It depends who you asked.

I was four when my father uttered a startling comment upon hearing the phone ring.

"I wonder which one of your mothers will pick up."

How confusing. He knew we had but one. However, by 26 I understood what he meant. The woman was blessed with multiple personalities. I was especially apprehensive of the Type A persona I labeled "Confident Frank," after her late father's pet name of "Frank" for her. The concept of being steam-rolled flat for four solid months wasn't appealing in the least. I secretly doubted that I'd last a month.

As Mom didn't acknowledge her multiple personalities, any thoughts of a struggle wouldn't occur to her. She was a positive soul and we were family. Hiring me meant I could earn the funds required to get on with my life. Having the extra help over the summer would be an added bonus. Of course I'd last the full four months.

Regardless of how I began working at FROG on May 2, 1983, it's staggering that neither of us remotely considered the one thing that could potentially ruin everything.

The fact that I knew little about Asian antiques and cared for them even less.

God help us.

CHAPTER 3

It's All Bard's Fault

Mom's affinity for Asian antiques began years earlier. I was six when she seized the opportunity to finally earn a university degree. Even though she'd endured a brief nursing career prior to marriage, Mom always felt "a little less" when in the company of more educated folk, and now that the three of us were in school, my father encouraged her to "take the odd history course." Mom opted for something bigger. She enrolled as a first-year student in the University of British Columbia's department of Fine Arts. A move I totally took for granted. Didn't everyone's mother enter university at 40 in 1962?

I didn't pay much attention to her fondness for Asian art until I was 12 and she suggested the inconceivable.

"I'd like to do something totally different today, kids. Instead of suntanning, let's scout out some Asian galleries and antique shops!"

Seriously? We were on vacation in Hawaii. It was Christmas. The last thing I wanted to do was wander aimlessly through dreary stores, staring at dusty old things I knew nothing about.

Thankfully my siblings were on the same page. Yanking on our bathing suits, we scooped up sunscreen, towels and straw mats, and fled. It was a wise call. When our parents finally returned ten hours later, Mom's behavior was most alarming. We froze as she flung herself upon the hotel bed, inexplicably sobbing.

"It was quite the day ... " Dad admitted while whipping up gin and tonics. He enjoyed several restorative sips before adding, "After spending the morning touring numerous galleries, we finally stopped for a quick bite. You can't beat the fresh papaya here on the islands ..."

"Geoff, my drink, please," Mom managed, holding out her hand.

He passed it over and then plopped down beside her. "The real fun began after lunch when we stumbled upon a small Asian antiques store called the Lantern Shop, tucked away in an outdoor mall. The chap who runs it was out but his wife Bette encouraged us to wait."

Mom nodded, the beverage clearly helping. I relaxed as she began speaking in a stronger voice.

"We were absolutely drained after spending so much time in the heat. So, we were thrilled when Bette generously offered us drinks, weren't we, Dad?"

"Yes. But things got a little tiresome after an hour. However, when I suggested that we come back another day, Bette drew closer, whispering she had a little secret. Bard had just received a large shipment from Japan. Of course, your mother persuaded her to let us have a peek at the unopened crates. Bette produced a crowbar and we were soon elbow-deep in treasure."

He paused to smile at us. "We especially loved the wooden chests called tansu. They were different sizes. While some had secret hidden compartments, they all had the most exotic iron locks. We fell in love instantly, didn't we, Mom?"

As that innocent tidbit triggered fresh tears, Dad rushed to explain.

"It was too difficult to zero in on just one. So ... we bought all seven."

The penny finally dropped. Our parents had spent our inheritance. And more.

As the three of us gasped, Dad simply patted Mom's arm.

"Relax, everyone. It's fine."

Dad described Bard's unfortunate reaction to his precious shipment being opened by the interlopers. The handsome, autocratic gent who was inordinately proud of his distant Germanic background, apparently morphed into a petulant child, stubbornly refusing to sell them anything. His plump and powdered wife salvaged the situation by calmly handing Bard a tall vodka tonic, which, along with two more, evidently worked wonders.

Mom smiled as Dad began to imitate Bard.

"'Frankie and Geoff, you're British aren't you? I love the British. I'm sensing you're kindred spirits and I'm never wrong about these things. Never. Now, I insist you be our guests for dinner at The Pacific Club. You won't get better food. Our club offers the best buffet on the islands. Let's meet there on Saturday night, at say, 7 p.m.? Excellent. Time for a top up. Come on Frankie, drink up, you're falling behind.'"

As 17-year-old Mike crowed over the hefty booze consumption, Dad reaffirmed Bard's refusal to discuss "anything tansu." It wasn't actually clear how many tansu my folks were buying, if indeed any. Everything might be sorted out over Saturday's dinner. If not, at least they'd enjoy "the best buffet on the islands."

Our parents brought us up to speed on Sunday morning.

When their hosts arrived at the club twenty minutes late, Bard blamed the delay on his wife's "damn inability to down her cocktail." Bette simply giggled and tucked her elbow into Mom's. "Ignore him. He's hungry. This way to the dining room, dear." She led them toward a wall of thick bamboo. "They've tweaked the foliage, I see. Nevermind. Come on, Frankie, just through here, dear," Bette tinkled.

Mom and Dad watched in dismay as their elegant hostess hitched up her muumuu. She then stepped boldly onto the raised bed and proceeded to battle her way through the luxuriant shrubbery like an intrepid safari guide.

"Your father motioned for me to follow. Someone had to. What if she got into trouble? Twisted an ankle or fell down? While Dad stayed with the furious Bard, I waded in. When we finally located a door, Bette hurled it open and toppled into the quiet dining room. Her satin slippers were ruined. I wiped away the largest of the muddy clumps and we joined Dad at Bard's table.

"Bard spewed a torrent of angry words at his wife. But she took no notice. She merely ordered a beverage round and the detour was soon forgotten. As Bard relaxed into his hosting role, he began extolling the highlights of the buffet and kindly introducing us to other club members. It wasn't until dessert that we finally got down to business. Tell the kids what he said, Dad."

My father grinned and began to bellow.

"'On behalf of my beautiful bride and myself, I'd like to extend a warm aloha to you both. May you fall under the spell of the islands and return to her shores many, many times. I have a sense that we're going to become great friends and I'm *never* wrong about these things. Never. For that reason, I have decided you may have all seven tansu.'"

Wendy, Mike and I stared at our parents in utter disbelief.

"Yes, all seven. I know. I nearly choked on my coconut chiffon slice. But there's more, isn't there, Geoff?"

Dad stood to deliver the denouement.

"After pausing to ensure our full attention, Bard continued, 'I quite understand how the acquisition of seven tansu could be prohibitive, so I'm prepared to make you a very special offer. Dear friends, you may buy them over time with absolutely no interest. Take as long as you need.'"

"Yes, he said it exactly like that. We couldn't believe the offer. Dad and I agreed on the spot before he could change his mind."

Thanks, Bard. The impact of these seven innocent tansu proved seismic. Our parents jettisoned most of their mid-century modern pieces in favor of Asian and Canadian antiques, rendering our home entirely different from those of my friends. I wasn't impressed, and while I ached for things to go back to normal, there wasn't a hope in hell of that happening. My parents were all in.

Shortly after that fateful purchase, Mom earned her master's degree in what was then called Oriental Art History. She accepted an offer to join the Fine Arts department as a lecturer, initiating six courses in the Art and Architecture of Latin America. Not her field, but nevermind. She managed to stay a few steps ahead of her students.

Life was good until, after eight years of lecturing at UBC, Mom was denied tenure due to regrettable internal politics. That stung. But it didn't defeat her. No, our indomitable matriarch announced her intention of breaking free from academia by opening an antique shop. And what did she know of business? Nothing. However, "Confident Frank" just knew she'd thrive selling her two favorite things: Asian and Canadian antiques. All she needed was a little seed money.

Now, here's a fine example of how we differ. If I needed a loan, I would have indulged in some hefty research and booked half-a-dozen different bank appointments. Not Mom. No. Our Confident

Frank just made a slight detour en route to the library. Spying a bank, she sauntered into the manager's office and favored him with a brief summation of her academic background and an outline of her plans for a quality antique shop. She wrapped the pitch by breezily announcing, "I should warn you. You'll only get my signature as security. No one else's. Just mine."

This was 1976, remember.

The astonished manager paused briefly before exclaiming, "I'm going to grant you a loan and I've no idea why."

She clearly bewitched him.

"Now, how much are you thinking, Frankie?" he asked, leaning forward with his pen poised over paper.

Mom didn't hesitate.

"$20,000."

"I'm sorry but you can't possibly start a business with that dismal amount. No. You'll need $100,000. I'll get the papers drawn up right now."

Mom has no recollection of continuing on to the library.

Armed with the $100,000, Frankie quickly signed the lease on a recently constructed 1,800-square-foot shop located just west of the popular Antiques Row, Vancouver's South Granville Street. She launched Frankie Robinson Antiques with a grand opening party two months later. Bard flew in from Honolulu as the guest of honor. His popularity dipped dramatically when he waltzed about the do, casting loud aspersions about the Canadian antique inclusions and warning that dealing in both cultures would only confuse people.

Unfortunately, the man was right. Frankie soon jettisoned the Canadian angle and tweaked the business's name to Frankie Robinson Oriental Gallery, focusing on antiques largely from China, Indonesia, Vietnam, Myanmar, South Korea and Japan.

She also added a less expensive line of modern collectibles from these countries. Bingo. Our gal could sell and the business began to take off. If you wanted something different, something of quality and something Asian, Frankie Robinson Oriental Gallery was the store to check out. By the end of its first year in business FROG was remarkably turning a profit.

As for me, well, I'd graduated from university and was enjoying my carefree 20s, living alone, and carving out a career packaging and selling a variety of province-wide coach tours to local seniors' groups. The fact that my artistic mother was running a successful business meant little. However, I like to think that had Mom been selling something I cared for, I'd surely have been a bit more attentive.

After successfully running FROG for seven years, Frankie ran into a rather serious roadblock when the Canadian Government tinkered with the tax laws. Now, to qualify as a deduction, an artifact had to be created by a living Canadian artist. With antiques no longer applicable, FROG's profits plummeted. Mom realized major changes were needed. She closed the store, took a few months off and then reopened FROG in a tiny 600-square-foot shop, on West 10th Avenue, three blocks south, at one-third her original rent. I would join her there three months later.

CHAPTER 4

All Aboard

FROG's previous location could not be more different than the current one. It would be like comparing a classic eighteenth century Chinese blackwood altar table with a 1960s folding TV tray table. While the original shop was a breezy L-shaped venue blessed with huge windows and a large, elegant washroom, this excessively tubular number could easily be mistaken for a tired train car. One-third the size of its predecessor, it boasted a deep set window at the front and a tiny office and cramped washroom at the back.

The smell was probably the first thing you noticed when you entered. I liked it. The dominant notes were that of floor wax, varnish and lacquer. The interior was so gloomy we had to install extra lights and keep them on throughout the day, even during the height of summer. Savvy customers left the sunglasses in the car. There was never any fear of being assaulted by our sound system, either. The tiny and rather ancient, burnt orange transistor radio tucked away on an office shelf was capable of spewing faint strains at best.

Only the very desperate were allowed access to the facilities, thanks to the clusters of tiny brown toadstools flourishing on one of the bathroom walls. When someone generously offered to scrape them off and whip up some "delicious risottos," we graciously declined, deeming it wise to avoid consuming unidentified fungi.

While Mom held fond memories of her previous location, she knew there was no point inquiring about recreating something similar here. Our Vancouver School Board landlord had lofty plans for a "sometime-in-the-future" demolition and would consider repairs only deemed absolutely necessary. Any redecorating efforts were the tenant's responsibility.

Frankie managed to perform miracles with the awkward narrowness of the showroom. Once the walls were repainted a flattering dove gray and the ceiling a pearly white, she oversaw the construction of a carpeted two-foot-high platform for the latter third of the shop, as well as a row of knee-high built-in cabinets along the entire length of the wall we shared with Fiona's travel agency. Meant for both storage and presentation, these would prove indispensable on the day of the infamous flood.

Everything faded to nothing in the low window, so Frankie ordered the construction of another elevated platform. Built from simple plywood, this one allowed the window pieces to be shown to their best advantage, particularly at night when the display became a true showstopper.

There were two advantages of this new venue over the old one. It came with a large outdoor parking lot and a devoted attendant. He consistently protected our two spaces like an eagle guarding its eaglets. No one could park there but us. While these stalls were adjacent to our back door, we always entered the shop through the front. Access through the back was impossible, thanks to surplus inventory, and the stacks of packing materials and various cleaning products. It's only now that I appreciate how truly blessed we were to be spared a fire.

The showroom was challenging. Of course, nothing showed to its full advantage when shoved into such a cramped space. We solved the problem by coming up with three other "showrooms," at no additional rent. The easiest alternative was the storefront sidewalk on dry days. When we sensed a customer's interest in a particular piece, Frankie or I would insist on dragging it outside. It was remarkable how things shone when they were allowed to stand alone, away from the cluttered distraction of everything else.

My parents' home on Tolmie Street stood in for the second alternative showroom. It was particularly popular after the arrival of large overseas shipments. Being only 15 minutes from the shop, Frankie often invited customers to come home with her for special previews.

The third alternative was Mom and Dad's hobby farm located in the countryside, some 45 minutes away. If customers felt special being invited to Tolmie, they surely felt so at the farm. Charmed by the pool, the cattle and the chickens, denying a purchase there often proved difficult to many.

CHAPTER 5

The Sensei

With the ceiling fixed and all of the inventory recovered from Fiona's, I was hiding out in the office a week later when there was a curious shift of energy out front. I slipped into the showroom to find Mom chatting animatedly with a pretty, conservatively dressed young woman. They were fawning over a pair of Chinese ancestor portraits.

As of just this morning, I knew ancestor portraits tended to be life-size paintings of venerated deceased family members and that it was rare to find a pair in good shape. Usually one was lost or they were damaged. This couple's overall severity spooked me and I couldn't imagine living with them on my walls. But maybe I was wrong. This gal thought they'd be perfect for her boyfriend's living room.

"I'm delighted to hear that, Doris. However, as I mentioned, I found these two languishing in a back alley shop in Hong Kong and dropped them off at our framers last week. They've just come back this morning. I've got several people interested in them. Is it possible for your boyfriend to come into the shop today, do you think? It would be a shame if he missed out."

As Mom paused, I also stared hopefully at Doris. Her boyfriend sounded interesting.

"Geez, yeah that'd be awful if he missed out. Could I use your phone, Jackie? He's really busy, but hopefully he can slip away for a bit."

I ushered Doris into the office and her excitement was palpable.

"Hi Ben. Sorry to disturb you, honey, but I've found the perfect paintings for your feature wall. Yes, for over the couch. They're of an old Chinese man and woman and the size and colors are just perfect. You have to come and see them. Now. Before someone else snaps them up."

Doris giggled as she hung up. "Jackie, would you be able to hang them if he likes them? Ben's not too handy with a hammer."

Neither was my mother. That sort of job usually fell to my father, the workaholic pediatrician who happily moonlighted as both deliveryman and handyman when time allowed. Hopefully he'd be available if needed. I didn't fancy attempting to hang them as they weighed a ton.

I had to admit this encounter was quite something. There'd been none of the usual questions regarding an item's authenticity nor any queries regarding their price. Over 150 years old and in mint condition, Mom was asking $2,500 for the pair.

A low slung, icy blue Mercedes soon purred to the curb out front. As Doris rushed outside, a pasty-looking fellow in his 50s slid from the driver's side.

My hopes for a younger candidate were dashed as she enfolded the stout little man in an enthusiastic embrace. He brushed her off impatiently.

"I don't have much time. Show me the paintings."

"Of course. Right this way, darling."

"Them?" Ben's hooded eyes flicked at the portraits before he grabbed the typed price tag. Stifling an audible hiss, he jabbed a stubby finger at the female portrait. Mom hustled over with her hand outstretched.

"Hello, you must be Ben. Welcome. I'm Frankie. As I'm sure you're aware, one has to be careful with such delicate pieces of artwork even when under glass. Let me tell you a little bit about the couple. See how they have the same embroidery on the sleeves and how their chairs are also similar? Those are some of the many clues they're a pair."

She'd clearly lost him at "Frankie." The man turned impatiently to his girlfriend.

"Where's this Jackie fella, Doris? I wanna talk to the owner about these."

Interesting. How would Mom handle this particular twist? Over the past three weeks I'd seen some fancy stickhandling through a few awkward roadblocks but never a blatant dismissal like this.

Subtly optimizing her 5-foot, 6-inch height, my mother slowly squared her shoulders and straightened her spine. She reached around and jammed both hands under her shirtdress's belt at the back. The dress, a cotton classic from Finnish design house Marimekko, was a staple in her FROG wardrobe. She had at least eight of them in various colors. Today's number was periwinkle blue and a crisp white.

With her elbows now jutting out sideways, Frankie's centuries-old, moss-colored jade bracelets slid down her right arm and clinked together loudly. She acquired the rare, oval-shaped pair in China years ago and never took them off. They proved most useful when we got separated in crowds. I simply had to shut my eyes and hone in on their unique sound which could be quite abrasive to the uninitiated.

As Ben glared at her wrist in irritation, my mother rocked back and forth on her heels, and flashed a broad smile. The poor man had no idea what he'd unleashed.

"Ben, I'm *Frankie*, the owner. This is my shop." Mom tossed back her head and paused to let that tidbit sink in. "I've been in business for the past seven years and prior to that I was a professor for eight in the Fine Arts department at the University of British Columbia. Both of my degrees are in Oriental Art History."

Ben's eyes widened. Frankie sailed on unabated.

"My husband and I started buying Asian pieces in the '60s. This business is my way of sharing my love and appreciation of them with others." She stepped away from the startled couple and spread her arms wide. "I do know Asian art."

It was beyond impressive. This particular persona, one I'd secretly call "The Sensei," the Japanese word for teacher, effectively elevated my boss's image beyond that of a simple shopkeeper and trounced any doubts about her credibility. With Doris now staring wide-eyed and Ben stunned into silence, Frankie graciously turned back to the portraits.

"Now, let's have a look at the provenance of this important and worthy pair, shall we? As I'm sure you know, to be deemed antique, a piece must be over 100 years old ..."

Dad agreed to install the ancestor portraits on Ben's feature wall that very evening.

CHAPTER 6

Wait. What?

That glorious epiphany about enjoying my FROG summer stint? Poof. Gone in a blink. All because of a woeful reality. I couldn't sell. I'd sold not one thing since signing on. Nothing. It was painful. I'd sold dozens of packaged bus tours in my previous job and simply assumed it would be the same here. But no. It seemed the harder I tried, the worse it got. Customers now bolted upon my approach as if I'd slapped a huge "RUN FOR YOUR LIVES" banner on my forehead.

In hindsight, there were plenty of reasons as to why I was struggling. Top of the list was my failure to recognize we were selling things that folks didn't actually *need*, and offering them at a high price point, *already used*. I hadn't the foggiest notion that to be successful here you had to sell the benefits of ownership. Of course, that can only happen when you know what you're selling and I hadn't a clue.

That was about to change.

Mom was out when the couple bustled in over the noon hour. I immediately recognized the woman. She and Frankie were swooning over a pair of antique Japanese temple candlesticks just yesterday. Carved from wood, they featured spindly three-foot pillars jutting out of chunky chrysanthemum bases. I thought they were particularly ugly and ancient. Their gold leaf coating was shedding like bark on an arbutus tree. However, the customer loved them and vowed to bring her husband in for a peek. This must be him.

The gentleman didn't have the same initial reaction as his wife. I bristled as he deliberately examined them from every angle and manfully hefted their weight, before finally deigning to acknowledge my presence.

"Okay, so enlighten me. Why are these $1,500 for the pair? I mean come on, what am I missing?"

Maybe it had something to do with their rarity and age? God only knew. My blank stare sparked a battery of questions.

"And why does the price tag mention candlepower? What's that? Is this real gold leaf? What was their purpose in the temple? Did you buy them in Japan?"

As my face bloomed a guilty scarlet, he smirked triumphantly, grabbed his disappointed wife's hand and sailed out the door. That was the last we saw of the couple. Ever.

I now felt quite ill. Why hadn't I made an effort to learn about the damn things? I cringed knowing they'd be happily ensconced in a new home if Mom had been here. If these past three weeks had taught me anything, it was that Frankie could sell. She was a natural.

I was suddenly reminded of my mother's extraordinary mink fur dress. I must have been around 10 when Mom bought it. Constructed in huge natural brown and dyed white squares, its uncanny resemblance to a furry chessboard for the visually impaired was spoiled by the wide gold zipper running down the length of the front. Mom was crazy about the dress. We were not. Finally fed up with our mean-spirited comments, she placed a sales ad in the local newspaper.

Mom hurled the lone respondent into the dress and plunked her in front of a full-length mirror before the woman could blink. "You look absolutely stunning. Oh, I *am* jealous. It doesn't look nearly as good on me. And just think, you'll never need a coat, you'll be cozy whenever you wear it!" Mom chirped as the potential purchaser preened. A final spin before the bedroom mirror and the woman was sold. Nevermind that the dress looked as equally dreadful as it did on the seller, she viewed it through Mom's lens and loved it. When our mother waved the dress goodbye and tearfully muttered that the slight profit gave her nothing but "cold comfort," we still couldn't believe the miracle. We were certain that she'd be saddled with the monstrosity forever.

The memory of that masterful effort got me thinking about our vastly different spending attitudes. Mom is a shopaholic, a truth solidly backed up in her diaries. The pages are rife with purchases, not only for her but also for friends and family. Buying something bestows upon her a euphoric high similar to those achieved with sugar or alcohol. Back in '83, I couldn't be more different. I couldn't understand why anyone would consider forking over the big bucks when they could get something similar for much cheaper elsewhere. That unfortunate attitude had me botching yet another sale, not long after the candlestick affair.

It involved a sweet elderly couple. Rather than greet these regular customers with a pleasant welcome, I barked, "Mom's at the bank, she'll be back soon." The husband recovered quickly and gently reassured me that he was certain I'd be able to help.

"Our bed is literally covered in pillows. We hurl them onto the floor at nighttime and they've become a tripping hazard. We need to store them in something that's both large and decorative. Do you have such a thing?"

We did. There were several candidates amongst the mizuya tansu (kitchen chests) and the Chinese cabinets. However, rather than mention them, I urged these lovely folks to pop over to their local Swedish furniture store, where I was certain they'd find the perfect cupboard and at a better price. The couple exchanged startled looks and the husband murmured, "Thank you. Perhaps it would be better if we came back when your mother's here."

They beetled out like rats from a burning dumpster. Right. Time to smarten up, Kelly. In addition to making an effort with the inventory and learning a few of Mom's nifty sales techniques, we could now add the overhauling of my attitude to money. What a daunting list; I'd be lucky to tackle a fingernail's worth by September. I decided to narrow it down to a few sensible goals.

The first one was switching out what I called my boss. "Mom" wasn't cutting it. Folks tended to abandon me when I addressed her as that. Of course they did. Why deal with the daughter who "probably can't find work elsewhere" when the savvy mother is on site? Calling her Frankie didn't sit right, though. It felt unnatural and forced. I opted for her family nickname of "Francine" instead.

On to the second tweak. My reaction to my appearance. I was 26 and looked 15. Not surprisingly, customers often dismissed me with a terse "just looking, thanks." That hurt. However, instead of retreating into my usual grumpy sulk, I'd try engaging them with a little random chit chat.

And finally, whenever someone bleated about a piece being too expensive (which happened often), instead of immediately falling mute, perhaps I could lean into Francine's breezy refrain of, "Well, we'd be happy for you to pay for it on the 'Never, Never, Hardly Ever' (NNHE) payment plan. We don't worry about interest. Just split your payments to suit you. Better yet, if you give us a series of post-dated checks, the piece can go home with you today."

Of course, the Never, Never, Hardly Ever originated with Bard's generous offer to let my parents pay for all seven tansu over time without interest. I now appreciated how this was far more than a simple sales ploy. As with Bard, it was truly important to Mom that the carefully sourced treasures find their proper homes. The NNHE plan enabled this to happen, regardless of a customer's financial situation.

Arming myself with these three goals was one thing, sharing them with my boss was quite another. In the end, I revealed just two, believing that any more would expose how pathetically inadequate I felt. My ego couldn't stand that. Mom learned I'd be calling her Francine from now on and that I was open to learning a little bit more about FROG's inventory.

Francine reacted to both with delight. She immediately thrust several heavy books at me, briskly advising that my homework for the week was to brush up on jade and the history of tansu. Clever gal. The books were blessed with colorful photos and easy to read descriptions.

CHAPTER 7

Coming Up Peaches

Despite my best efforts, it was now June and I was still struggling to make my first sale, when a girl of about my own age crept into the shop. With Francine out on the 3 p.m. tea run, I prayed that I wouldn't be asked the unanswerable. However, as the newcomer hovered gingerly up front, flipping price tags and sighing, I felt as if I was spying on a hungry and wary deer in a populated glen. She wanted to flee but needed to stay. I had to end her misery.

"Hi. Welcome. If you're looking for smaller, more reasonably priced pieces, we've stashed them here in the back. Those heavier, pricier numbers are to deter the shoplifters."

She reluctantly turned toward me.

"I'm looking for a wedding present but I don't think I'll find anything here. I want to keep it to $100."

The girl's words tumbled out in such a heated rush, I could barely understand her. Such discomfort was truly bolstering; the way forward was suddenly clear. After fumbling with the lock on one of the glass cabinets, I gestured toward the shelf of colorful, life-sized, ceramic peaches.

"Have a gander at these. They're over 100 years old so they're genuine antiques. I think one could work as a gift. The peach is an iconic symbol of longevity in Chinese culture. You'd not only be giving the happy couple something other than the ubiquitous toaster oven, but you'd also be blessing them with wishes for a long and happy marriage. I'm sure they'd treasure it and would always remember your thoughtfulness. Better yet, they're priced at $100. I believe we're the only shop in Vancouver that sells them so it would truly be a unique gift."

She looked interested, so I awkwardly shoved the largest peach into her hand, silently imploring her to like it. As she slowly rotated it, I grew dizzy awaiting the verdict.

"I agree. It would be perfect. Thank you so much for your help. I've been looking for ages for just the right thing. I'll take it!"

Good Lord. I'd done the impossible. I'd finally sold something. I couldn't wait to tell Francine.

I was positively reborn. Having experienced the euphoric rush that accompanies a sale, I wanted more of it and doubled down on the self-improvement efforts. Over the ensuing weeks, I gradually grew more comfortable with both the inventory and their prices. Of course you'd expect to pay more for something that had survived for a hundred years.

Customers were also responding favorably to my Francine references and while nobody remarked that I looked older, I felt it. Most days. All of these tiny personal victories boosted my confidence and led to a glorious flurry of small sales. While nothing was over $250, it was gratifying that my presence was finally making a positive difference.

CHAPTER 8

A Private Screening

Not long after the wondrous peach sale, Francine startled me with a proposition that would have been unthinkable just mere weeks earlier.

"Let's organize some routine days off, Kel. You take Thursdays and I'll do Fridays, that way we could each get a breather before our busy Saturdays."

It was a solid acknowledgment of my recent efforts. However, I was nervous. Up until now, I'd never worked more than an hour by myself, let alone a full day. Thankfully, my first solo Friday was a soggy one and I was desperate for company by the time the first customer toddled in around 3 p.m. Despite having never met the 60ish, burly and florid fellow before, I reacted with all the ebullience of a dog greeting her master after a lengthy absence.

"How lovely to see you. Welcome, welcome! Are you on a mission?"

The unique question stunned the poor chap for a second or two.

"You must be Kelly. I'm Mrs. Shell's husband. She's sent me in to check out your new screen shipment."

What a relief. I was familiar with Mrs. Shell's quest for the right screen. While Chinese antique screens could run as large as twelve panels, the bulk of our recent arrivals were six and eight panels, a more suitable size for homes. His wife wanted one that was at least eight feet long when spread out flat. I mentally scrolled through the potential options currently stacked against the wall and came up with two that might fit the bill. Could I actually deal with this by myself? I had to try. I willed myself to act as if discussing screens was as normal to me as chowing down a bag of potato chips.

"If you'll just stand over there, Mr. Shell, I'll spread them out and then let you have a gander at your leisure."

Thankfully, the hinges on both of the eight-panel screens were intact, making it easy to crab-walk them to the opposite wall. After unfolding the panels and angling them to their best advantage, it was time to launch into what I dearly hoped would be an insightful spiel about what to look for when considering a Chinese *coromandel* screen.

It was positively surreal to hear my voice wax on about how the delicate design of flowers, birds, people and temples was actually carved down into layers of lacquer over a softwood core, and how more panels meant a heavier screen; pertinent details I'd acquired the day before.

With the voices in my head now bellowing to "stop nattering," I fled to the other side of the room and discreetly wiped my sweaty palms on my cotton skirt. It was important for Mr. Shell to ponder in peace.

"Oh, I do like that one."

I shot down and snatched an imaginary blob of mud off the floor in an effort to compose myself. Mr. Shell preferred the superior and most expensive of the two. It was $1,800. But I mustn't get ahead of myself. I must react as serenely as the Reverend Mother when the Nazis are pounding on her Abbey door in *The Sound of Music.*

Duly fortified, I channeled my inner Francine.

"You're welcome to take it home and try it out on approval for a few days, Mr. Shell."

"Really? That would be most helpful. However, it's far too big for my vehicle. Do you by any chance provide delivery? If so, we're home tonight. Would that work?"

Bless him, he was oblivious to the fact that I'd gleefully heft the bulky delight over on my back, if need be. We settled on a delivery time of 7 p.m.

I started getting ready rather early that evening, despite knowing it would take me just thirty minutes to drive to his house in West Vancouver. It was a smart move. The intact screen proved too big for my three-door hatchback. I had to dismantle it and load the eight panels separately. Putting it back together outside the Shell's home would also require extra time.

Wrestling several stubborn pins from their hooks chewed up a good twenty minutes. When I finally managed to get all eight panels free, I carefully nestled each one between a layer of thick towels and placed them into the back of my car. Unfortunately, the last two would only cooperate when flipped sideways and wedged up against the windshield. The resulting vision loss meant the total elimination of right-hand turns, but no matter. It was refreshing to focus on something other than not coming across as a incompetent, nervous ninny to the Shells.

I arrived with fifteen minutes to spare only to discover that some thoughtless fool had plunked their squat black sedan in the middle of the shared driveway, leaving me the only option of parking on the road above. There was no way I could lug the whole thing down from there in one go. It was far too heavy.

The eight toe-pinching trips gobbled up a chunk of the remaining time. As I prepared to reassemble the screen outside the Shells' front door, I suddenly remembered the credit card machine under my front seat. By the time I scrambled back down with the bulky apparatus, sweat was not only beading on my forehead but also puddling under my arms. It was now just past 7. I'd have to reassemble the damn thing inside. I swiped frantically at my damp forehead with the sleeve of my jacket before stabbing at the illuminated doorbell button.

Mr. Shell greeted me warmly.

"My wife's just popped over to her sister's. I expect she'll be back soon, Kelly. Come on through and I'll show you where we're thinking it might work."

He led the way through the high-ceilinged foyer into a tastefully decorated den blessed with south-facing windows and a small fan dispatching a welcome breeze about the room. The ocean view was breathtaking.

"We thought the screen could go here." Mr. Shell pointed to a large unadorned wall opposite the windows and my hopes soared. The screen should be a knockout there. I discreetly swiped at the sweat now coursing down the back of my neck, nearly dropping the slippery credit card machine in the process.

"Let's just put that thing over here," my observant host advised, indicating the exquisite Chinese antique blackwood coffee table which I instantly pegged to be worth around $2,500. I placed the machine carefully on top, only to inwardly cringe. It stood out like a beacon. I began to babble. He mustn't think I thought the sale was a certainty.

"Of course, the screen is strictly here on approval, Mr. Shell. You must live with it for at least a day or two before you decide whether it'll become a permanent fixture. It won't take me two seconds to put it together again. Perhaps you'd be kind enough to guard our credit card machine while I retrieve the panels."

"Guard our credit card machine?" Could I have said anything more lame? I flashed him an apologetic smile and fled. By the time I'd hauled in the final panel there was no way to hide the rivulets of sweat now streaming down my face and I accepted the proffered box of tissues with open gratitude.

Acknowledging my determination to complete the setup by myself, Mr. Shell settled into an armchair and readjusted the fan. It was now blowing directly upon him. The room grew warmer by the second and the half-assembled number threatened to topple over several times but I stuck to it. When I finally managed to string them together, I stretched the screen out in a suitable accordion fashion, struggled out of my now sodden jacket and slowly backed up to the windows. The screen was truly magnificent when viewed from this distance; the inlaid mother of pearl figures positively gleamed against the black lacquer background. I shot a confident look at my host but was startled to find his attention firmly focused on his slippered feet.

Had I somehow completely misjudged the overall impression? No. The coromandel screen belonged there. It was perfect. I rushed to fill the awkward silence.

"This is a temple garden scene. Note how the people are gathering in a cohesive unit under the trees. The soaring cranes represent longevity and the shimmering circles symbolize pearls of wisdom ..."

The poor man was now truly struggling. His eyes darted about the room, capable of looking anywhere but at me. I was about to suggest the unthinkable, that of physically shifting the screen to a different location when he suddenly stirred.

"I like it. Yes, it's perfect. I'll just get my card and we can settle up right now." He bolted from the room.

I'd done it. I'd sold the behemoth. But to a man who suddenly couldn't look at me. Whatever was the matter? When he slipped back into the room, I found myself talking exceptionally slowly, in those silky British tones I involuntarily adopted in times of stress. "Well, that is just capital. I'm positively chuffed. Now, if you'd be so kind, please just pop your card here into the machine ..."

With his head cranked to the side and my hands shaking uncontrollably, we were quite the pair. Mr. Shell blindly scratched out a wobbly signature, nodded twice and then tiptoed out of the room. Okay, then. I ripped out his copy of the slip, scooped up my jacket and the machine, and trundled behind him to the foyer. The front door was closed with the slightest of whispers. I was dismissed.

I bolted back up to my car and hurled myself into the front seat, desperate to reflect on what the hell just happened. His behavior was so odd: warm and welcoming one minute, cold and dismissive the next.

A chill swept over me. It was probably the onset of shock. Reaching for my ruined jacket that was still wrapped protectively around the credit card machine, I experienced a startling ease of movement. It was almost as if I were naked.

A quick glance down and the sorry truth became clear. Good Lord. The physical excursion of manhandling the panels had my blouse's eight buttons scattering like teeth in a hockey fight. My once white, now off-gray cotton bra was on full-frontal display. Poor Mr. Shell had been given one hell of a private screening. Should I go back and apologize and hunt down said buttons? Absolutely not. Neither he nor I would cope well with a recovery mission. I'd simply toss the shirt. I couldn't bear to look at it again, much less wear it.

With one hand on the wheel and the other clutching my gaping blouse together, I eased into the line of cars slowly shuffling over the Lions Gate Bridge and I couldn't help but grin. My previous sales record was shattered by a whopping $1,500. Francine was going to be thrilled. Perhaps I'd just save some of the more colorful details for one of those long dreary afternoons in the shop when we could both do with a laugh.

CHAPTER 9

One Little Pig

When Mrs. Shell phoned the next morning to tell me how much she loved the screen, there was no mention of my unfortunate flashing. I wasn't surprised. Her husband was a gentleman. Francine was thrilled about the sale and assured me that I could do it again. Let's hope so. Preferably without additional button losses.

My attitude toward the job continued to shift. These eight weeks in, I felt less like bolting for the backroom when someone ventured in while on my own. While still steadfastly refusing to call her "Mom" in the shop, I also no longer balked at revealing that Francine was my mother. I'd finally accepted that being the boss's daughter granted me a cachet that I'd otherwise not enjoy. It eased the awkwardness with new customers, especially when I wove it into the conversation early on. Folks invariably commented about how lucky I was to have grown up with Asian antiques. I felt no compunction to divulge that my appreciation of Asian art was just developing.

On the day that the tall, slender and well-dressed woman in her mid-50s came in and immediately asked for Frankie, I felt none of the previous jealousy. I simply replied, "She's off today. I'm her daughter, Kelly. Welcome."

"Oh, how nice to meet you. I'm Margaret McKenzie. I'm hoping to find something that could brighten up my living room mantle."

That depth of information was refreshing; few customers were as specific. I left her to poke about on her own and she found something quickly.

"What can you tell me about this plate, Kelly?" She asked, pointing to an item we were selling on consignment.

"It's an antique Chinese celadon porcelain plate. Celadon refers to the green color of the glaze."

Her receptive eyes encouraged me to say more.

"The value is both in the glaze and the fact that the plate is in mint condition with no cracks or chips."

"Oh, I know celadon. It's lovely, isn't it? I'll take it, thank you. It'll be perfect for our mantle."

Another treasured piece had found a worthy home.

But then Mrs. McKenzie uttered the unexpected.

"I was actually your mother's very first customer in this location."

She what? No.

I remembered that visit even though it occurred before I joined FROG. Francine had called me right after with some disturbing information.

"I've got good news and bad news, Kel. The good news is that I've just made my first sale here! The bad news is what sold. I'm sorry, love, but your pig is gone…"

I was devastated. The polished, brown, stone Chinese antique pig was the first thing I'd truly liked of FROG's. About the size of a large chicken egg, the creature was blessed with a wrinkled snout, broad mouth and delicately etched trotters. The carver clearly understood pigs. I adored all things porcine and this feisty little number was destined as one of the anchor pieces of my new collection. Unable to afford it, I'd arranged to pay for it on the NNHE and stubbornly insisted that it remain in the store until the last payment.

"I'm so sorry, Kel. I know how much you wanted it," Francine admitted. "However, I assure you that it's gone to a good home. A very nice woman bought it as a spirit booster for her son who's in the hospital."

"He'd damn well better appreciate it," I snarled.

I still ached to know if he did. But I dare not ask. Not after what had happened a few days ago with Mrs. Tungsten, one of my least favorite customers.

Conversation with the sour-faced soul always stalled within minutes. I was determined that this visit would be different.

"Cherie was in yesterday," I volunteered.

The woman skewered me with a gaze worthy of her last name and asked if her adult daughter had bought anything.

"Yes, a blue and white bride's jar."

Mrs. Tungsten's eyebrows shot into her hairline and she began peppering me with questions.

"How much was it? Is it for herself or is it a gift? Did Cherie pay with cash or with a credit card?"

Francine to the rescue. She grabbed the inquisitor by the elbow and gently steered her toward the door.

"I am sorry, Mrs. Tungsten, but we're closing early today. Kelly and I need to prep for an important appraisal. Lovely to see you, enjoy the rest of your day, dear."

The woman was royally dispatched.

"Boy, nice quick-witted thinking, Francine," I squeaked, still recovering.

My mother rounded on me with a face the color of steamed beets.

"Christ! What a mess. I thought you understood that you *never* discuss a sale with anyone but the purchaser," Francine hissed.

Oh my God. This wasn't the usual "you're skating on thin ice," or "you're sailing close to the wind, my dear" warning. This was full blown fury.

She began to pace about the shop like a pent-up tiger.

"You've really put the cat amongst the pigeons, Kelly. I never reveal *anything* to that woman. Christ! Poor Cherie. She'll be hounded by that old goat."

Whoa, this was next level. Francine never criticized a customer like this.

"I'm so sorry, Mom. I didn't think beyond making random conversation," I bleated.

"That's obvious," Francine snapped.

I must have looked truly penitent for my mother stopped pacing and sat next to me.

"Look," she began, struggling to rein in her impatience. "It's not just about Mrs. Tungsten being a busybody and hounding her daughter…"

No?

"It's also about the need to respect our customer's privacy. A sale is always a private matter, Kelly, and not unlike doctor-patient confidentiality. Honestly, we never know the real reason behind a purchase. Yes, Cherie said she was buying the bride's jar for herself, but was she really? It might be a gift for her friend, or her husband, or a lover, or even, God forbid, her mother."

Francine acknowledged my giggles with a hand flap.

"I know, it's a stretch. However, it's possible. And we're not done."

Of course we weren't.

"What if Cherie did buy it for herself despite financial restrictions on the homefront? Lord knows I've encountered that myself a few times. If she's like me, she'll tuck it away for a few months. But who knows? We don't. Nor should we. But you can bet that Mrs. Tungsten won't rest until she does. She'll pester the poor girl relentlessly." Francine paused briefly before delivering the denouement. "I doubt Cherie will ever consider buying from FROG again."

Message received. Big time.

With that lambasting still fresh on my plate, I skated far away from the pig or Mrs. McKenzie's son. It would be a long while before I would discuss purchases or anything personal with customers, thank you very much, regardless of who instigated the conversation.

As she made to leave, Mrs. McKenzie commented on the number of pieces tagged with stickies labeled Designer Show House. I explained that they'd been selected by local interior designers for an upcoming fundraiser, and she nodded. She knew of it. Her husband, a much sought-after general contractor, was orchestrating the exhaustive renovation of the stately home that would house the fundraiser. That coincidence soothed my ruffled soul and we parted on good terms.

It would be four long years later, and thanks to someone other than Mrs. McKenzie, that I finally learned the true fate of *my* darling little pig.

CHAPTER 10

Our Fred

While I was Francine's first employee on the payroll, she had long enjoyed the voluntary services of another. My father, Geoff. An eminent pediatrician, he was at the forefront of Fetal Alcohol Syndrome research in Canada. When time allowed, he also made deliveries and served as her handyman.

A workaholic, Dad was a perceptive, shy and humble fellow who bore an uncanny resemblance to the silver-haired Robert Young of TV's Marcus Welby MD fame. Unlike our gregarious Francine, Dad was happiest flying under the radar. In the early days of FROG, only the most trusted customers learned his real name, and even fewer discovered that he was actually Francine's husband and a doctor; most simply knew him by the pseudonym Fred. Blessed with a wicked sense of humor, he delighted in making the FROG deliveries wearing the special pair of overalls given to him by Francine. Striped blue and white, their front pocket sported a large, red thread "FRED" label.

One of my most favorite memories of Dad as Fred The Delivery Man took place on a hot Saturday in July of 1983. A designer sent in his client, Dr. Humbert, to look at several carpet options. After a ponderous hour, he finally zeroed in on an exquisitely hand-knotted, antique number, comprised of deep blues and reds. When Francine suggested that the doctor take the bulky item home on approval, she sweetened the offer by throwing in the services of her delivery man. The good doctor accepted on the condition that she tag along as well.

When our trusty Fred and his small serviceable red truck arrived promptly at 5 p.m., he broke into a huge grin upon learning the customer's identity.

"I know Cecil. Good thing I wore the overalls, I doubt he'll recognize me," Dad exclaimed with a laugh.

Thinking he simply looked like the Saturday version of himself, I was skeptical that a name change and overalls would make much difference. But whatever. After helping heft the heavy roll into the back of the truck, I zipped home, kicked off my heels and got into my sweats.

Francine checked in by phone some two hours later. She sounded tired.

"The rug is perfect. The colors blended seamlessly with the azure walls. I knew it the second your father unfurled it at the bottom of the foyer stairs. But Dr. Humbert didn't. No, the man's a ditherer. I'm not being unkind, it's the truth. Not only did he not recognize Dad, he insisted on seeing the rug in multiple spots. Your father lugged it all over the house before the doctor finally conceded that he'd best leave the decision to his designer."

The fellow must have been quite overwhelmed with the whole process to not recognize a colleague.

"Your father was an absolute angel. He kept his cool the entire time. I've no idea how."

I chuckled, knowing Dad would have enjoyed every deceptive minute.

"We were heading for the truck when Dr. Humbert called out with a drink offer."

"So he did recognize Dad?" I asked.

Mom ignored the question.

"I sank into a lawn chair in his shady backyard and Dr. Humbert beckoned Dad to join him by the pool. I assumed it was to take drink requests, but no. After fishing about in a pocket, the doctor pressed a limp $10 bill into your father's palm."

"What?"

"Oh wait. There's more. Dr. Humbert patted him on the back and said, 'There's a good man, Fred, now go and wait in your truck. Frankie will join you once she's finished her drink.'"

"Oh my god."

"I know! Can you imagine? Of course, Dad was a bloody marvel. He didn't say a word. Just nodded at us both and left. I've never guzzled a drink so quickly in my life!"

"What happened when you got back to the truck?"

"We mutely sailed away from the curb. Your father is going to be dining out on that $10 tip story forever."

He most certainly was.

While Dad found the Humbert rug situation to be both amusing and lucrative, he did have his limits.

The following Saturday, Francine spent a good part of the afternoon chatting with a young South American who was familiar with her former UBC gig. He tried to sell her several ceramic beads from his private collection but she wasn't interested.

"Nevermind. I've got others at home. Perhaps they'll be more to your liking."

Francine's noncommittal smile only spurred him further.

"Come to dinner tonight, ladies. Bring your husbands."

Always thirsty for new experiences, Francine agreed.

"Excellent. No need to bring anything. See you at 7."

We let ourselves in when no one answered our knocks. I was shocked. This wasn't the cozy dinner I was expecting. This was dinner for sixty of bead boy's dearest bohemian pals. The room was packed with folks who were either lounging languidly on mattresses strewn about the floor or dancing around in joyous abandonment. No one appeared to be older than 30.

While Dad and I struggled to adjust, Francine made a beeline for the only piece of furniture in the entire room. A tall, wooden kitchen stool. She joyfully scrambled up and announced her intention to remain there "for the rest of the night."

Excellent.

My father looked at me helplessly.

"Why don't you nab that mattress over there, Dad? I'll hunt down some drinks," I suggested, rolling my eyes in Mom's direction.

He crawled onto the lumpy mattress and claimed it as our own.

The tiny kitchen boasted several large Styrofoam coolers, each stocked with beer and cheap wine. All we needed now was food. I snatched up a wooden bowl and filled it with the treats on offer: dried figs and cheese-flavored Ritz crackers. Dinner.

When I staggered back, my father was no longer alone. A vacant-faced, bare-chested fellow had joined him. I would have to sit on the floor.

The newcomer clearly thought Dad suffered from hearing problems for he suddenly hollered, "I'm high on life. And you? What's your bag?"

As the baritone query rocketed throughout the apartment, someone shut off the tunes. The mood shifted. Folks realized they were in the presence of an elder. He must be a guru! What words of wisdom would fall from his lips?

45

OUR FRED

I was on high alert for a different reason. My father hated this kind of attention. How the hell would he handle this novel inquiry? He was already pissed off. This whole event was far too "artsy fartsy" for his liking.

Dad slowly inched his way up the mattress until he could sit up against the wall. He then clasped his hands around the back of his head, and closed his eyes. Not good. I braced as everyone else leaned in as one, eager to catch each insightful syllable.

When he finally spoke, the delivery could not be more toneless. "I work ... in the back ... of my wife's ... shop."

We slipped out soon afterward. Any acquisition of those antique ceramic beads would have to take place at another time. Without Geoff. Or Fred.

CHAPTER 11

Mamasan Frankie

By the end of July, I was finally contributing more than just my personality to FROG's bottom line. While I hadn't scored anywhere near the $1,800 screen effort, I was managing to churn out sales in the range of $100 to $500.

How? Well, taking an interest in the inventory certainly helped. Sharing the potential uses for a piece now felt quite natural and enjoyable. Initially drawn to the quirky and fun contemporary numbers, such as the life-sized Thai reclining bronze pigs and the gigantic wooden chickens ("great decorative items"), I was beginning to also covet some of the antiques as well. Among my favorites were the Japanese silk obis ("wonderful table runners or wall art"), the Chinese blackwood altar tables ("the simple lines conjure up the mid-century modern pieces I grew up with") and the Japanese tansu ("unlimited storage options").

General chit chat with "the regulars" was also becoming easier, thanks in part to a nifty system of Francine's. Whenever customers volunteered unique personal information, such as Stacy couldn't drink coffee or else she'd shut herself up in the coat closet,

Susan was finally happily married to a fourth husband and Brian and Colin were struggling to adjust to their new life with a puppy from hell, Francine would record it onto file cards. I spent hours soaking up the information. Arming myself with these details made conversation with these folks so much easier, and I liked how it also helped to make them feel special and remembered.

These three months in, I was also gaining an understanding of how different an antique store's customer culture is to those of other retail shops. Of course, there's the hefty dose of looky-loos but among the serious purchasers there's very little grab, pay and dash away. Many of our customers tended to linger, some for hours. This was especially true on Saturdays, now my favorite day of the week at FROG. Francine encouraged me to always welcome the regulars, regardless of whether they had any intentions of buying. It was fine with her if they just wanted to have a chinwag and swap stories.

I was also learning that time passed slowly on the days when no one came in. In those early months at FROG, the down times were allocated to dusting, polishing, paying bills and alerting folks to impending shipment arrivals or price reductions. Our accountant took care of the rest, so once shopkeeping chores were taken care of, we teetered dangerously close to abject lethargy. Not a good place to be. Once there, it was extremely difficult to summon even a drop of enthusiasm when folks did venture in.

Francine and I recognized the need for diversion. We made up a game in which one of us would imitate a customer and the other had to guess the identity. This pastime was a godsend. While it usually left us giggling like naughty kids, it also kept us sharp and alert. I'd forgotten that my mother was a surprisingly gifted mimic. She nailed the impression of a certain fellow in his mid-40s who never actually bought from FROG but regularly favored us

with tales of his mother's "wonderful Asian antiques collection."
I still grin, picturing Francine waltzing about the shop, stabbing
her index finger at random pieces, exclaiming, "Mutha has that,
too, but of course hers is in better condition and is *much* bigger!"
However, not *all* was sweetness and light at this point in my
life at FROG. There were still several situations that got my
insecurities roaring back. One classic trigger was the besotted
Frankie fans. Especially the ones who were my age. They tended
to be the most dismissive of me. Rather than simply rise above
it, my fragile ego folded like a toppled screen. I became sullen
and unapproachable. Not a good look. Francine hadn't a clue.
She sparkled under all the attention, instantly morphing into a
figure of maternal benevolence and wisdom. I snarkily labeled
this persona "Mamasan Frankie."

A pattern for Mamasan Frankie quickly emerged. It always
opened with an effusive welcome.

"How lovely to see you! Let's pop around the corner to The
Granville Diner. You don't mind looking after the shop for a bit,
do you, Kel, dear? We won't be long."

Mind? I was both livid and resentful. "For a bit" meant at
least an hour and a half. And these guys were my age! They were
ignoring me as if I was their baby kid sister.

As I grudgingly held down the fort, stewing over the unfairness
of it all, Mamasan Frankie would soak up every minute revelation
on offer. She'd then shower the darlings with morsels of advice,
which would be carefully parsed, rated and sorted before the couple tumbled back into FROG exuding renewed vigor and joy.

"Sorry for being so naughty and staying out so long, Kelly,
dear!" my mother would trill.

I'd grit my teeth and her acolyte would titter. Every single time.
Mamasan Frankie would now fire up the booster rockets. She'd

turn to the devotee and say, "Let's forget about real life for a while and soak up some timeless pieces. They'll do wonders for your soul."

I'd retreat to the backroom, leaving the pair to traipse blissfully about the crowded inventory, giggling and whispering like teenagers. When the time for departure arrived, reluctant, heartfelt goodbyes would be exchanged and I'd be asked to escort the admirer to their car. They would always be accompanied by at least one item chosen especially for them by Mamasan Frankie. If they didn't buy it outright, they were encouraged to "live with it and let its healing energy work its magic."

Of course, deep down, I knew, as with all of her many different personas, this one was genuine. In that moment, Francine *was* Mamasan Frankie. The nudging toward a sale was a natural extension of her desire to provide comfort. It wasn't a ploy. Nor was the mothering. She simply couldn't help herself, a fact I was surprised to see acknowledged in a diary entry as: "I don't know why I interrupted Kelly's sales efforts by inviting Dee out to tea. I just did."

While that revelation was startling, it wasn't nearly as astonishing as the eagerness with which these folks shared every aspect of their lives with my mother. Francine and I had grown closer of late, but it was still difficult for me to open up and share my fears, failings or even hopes. Our family tended to deal with problems through humor and I'd always been intensely private. Toss in my perceived notion of my mother's incredible personal strength and success at whatever she touched, and my lips were sealed like barnacles on a dry rock.

Of course, intellectually I knew my mother understood that these people were aching for a connection with her, and that she also genuinely wanted to help them. As her daughter, though, I found this persona especially difficult to deal with. I was jealous and my reaction was admittedly immature. I deliberately iced her out. The more motherly she was to them, the colder I was to her. But nevermind. I only had to hold on for one more month.

CHAPTER 12

Diving in at the Farm

When Francine invited me to the small hobby farm (FROG's fourth showroom) for a Sunday swim, along with the ancestor portrait purchasers Doris and Ben, I begged off, even though I loved it there. Located in Abbotsford, just 30 miles east of Vancouver, it was the perfect spot for a mini-break with its pool, small vegetable garden, handful of hens and a half-dozen steer. However, I just wasn't up to a solid diet of Mamasan Frankie on my day off.

Doris was now quite the Mamasan Frankie fan. She and I barely spoke. With my return to university looming ever closer, I frankly saw no point in attempting to win her over. But I was curious as to why she accepted the widowed Ben's proposal after mere months of dating. I couldn't see it. While you couldn't fault his business acumen (the self-made multimillionaire was admired by many), he seemed somewhat taciturn and difficult to live with.

I also suspected my invite was partly due to Dad's attitude. He was neither a swimmer nor a sun worshiper. My suspicions that Mom feared the visit might veer sideways were instantly confirmed in her phone call later that night.

"The second I suggested a swim, your father shot off to pick berries for dessert. Thankfully, Doris didn't notice. She immediately produced their bathing suits, several fluffy thick towels and two different types of sunscreen. Ben's skin is very sensitive. His eyes are too. We had a brief moment of hysteria when his sunglasses went missing, but thankfully Doris found them on the front seat of their car.

"They settled around the pool. I opened a bottle of wine and brought out an assortment of crackers and cheese. I do wish you'd come, Kel. You'd have enjoyed yourself. It was really rather pleasant with the sun dancing on the water and the cows bellowing cheery greetings."

I wasn't convinced.

"Doris joined me for a dip. She's a dear. With Ben lolling about in his deck chair like some exotic lizard, she shared tidbits about her wedding dress. It sounds lovely. We covered the veil and shoe options, and I was about to inquire after their honeymoon plans, when Ben suddenly announced that he was going for a paddle."

She'd lost me at the veil and shoe options.

"Well, the poor man somehow slipped and plunged headfirst into the water. God knows how. Doris began shrieking bloody murder! I was quite concerned until he finally shot to the surface, all purple and gasping."

I was now fully present.

"Doris rallied and we somehow managed to haul Ben onto the deck. I insisted that he lie down on his side and Doris tried to help him. She jammed a towel underneath him and began patting him dry with another. It was all too much for the old boy. He suddenly reared up, roaring 'Goddamn it, woman! Leave me alone,' and collapsed into his chair, chest heaving."

"How scary! Did Dad come running?"

"Of course, not. But then Ben began acting very strangely. He leapt up, waggled his head, and shook his leg out sideways, like a rabid dog might do. Christ! I was just about to yell for help when Ben hollered, 'I'M COMPLETELY DEAF IN ONE EAR!'"

Francine's voice dropped below a whisper.

"Doris asked for some Q-tips."

Oh Lord, no. My practical father had long ago put the kibosh on things he considered "consumer crap" and Q-tips fell smack into the middle of that category. Francine would have more luck finding an ear syringe than a Q-tip.

"Unfortunately, Ben 'COULDN'T HEAR A GODDAMNED THING' for the rest of their visit and it was most unpleasant. Your father did little more than grin. I was absolutely drained by the time they went home. I don't know if I can work tomorrow. Jesus Christ Almighty."

I was slowly learning that selling antiques is about so much more than just selling antiques.

CHAPTER 13

The Origins of "Francine" and "Godfrey"

Once Dad learned about my new habit of calling Mom "Francine" while working at FROG, he encouraged me to use "Godfrey," our family's nickname for him. We both agreed it felt more natural than "Fred."

Curious regulars were soon asking me how the names came into being.

They originated in Hawaii.

A year after meeting Bard, we were back in Honolulu and renting a small apartment for a few weeks. Our landlords invited us to their son and daughter-in-law's annual Boxing Day party without informing the hosts. Donny and Janet were initially thrown by our presence, but after a quick huddle with his parents, they rallied and introduced us kids, Mike, Wendy and me, to the buffet table. It was a veritable wonder laden with gigantic platters of meat, baked goods, tropical fruit, a variety of salads and every conceivable option of chips.

"God, there's nothing to do here but eat. What happens when we're full?" my ever practical sister asked.

I'd no idea. Everyone else was over 50.

As Mom and Dad were swept into the heart of the festive knot of floral dresses and aloha shirts, Donny clapped his hands for attention.

"Happy Boxing Day, one and all! Welcome. We're joined today by our Canadian friends who are staying at my parents' rental over Christmas. Francine and Godfrey. Francine is the award-winning author of children's books and her husband Godfrey is a successful dentist. Please give them a warm aloha!"

I glanced at Mike and Wendy for clarity. Their huge grins confirmed it. Perhaps the party wouldn't be so dull after all.

As the booming "ALOHA" faded and everyone broke into small groups, a puffy-faced woman cornered our father. We shuffled closer.

"I'm so glad to meet you, Godfrey. I'm Lani. Could you take a quick peek at one of my molars? It really hurts. I can't sleep because of the throbbing. Sorry to bother you on your vacation but my dentist is with his family on the mainland. He won't be back until January."

Wendy, Mike and I were enthralled. Would Dad play along or admit the truth?

"Oh, there's nothing worse. I do wish I could help, Lani, but of course as a Canadian, I'm not licensed to practice here in the States. You should book an appointment with an emergency dentist. Or you could ask your physician to prescribe some strong painkillers to tide you over until your regular man returns. Make sure you also ask for some antibiotics, just in case ..." Dad advised. He was the right person to ask, having just recovered from two emergency root canals.

Lani nodded in confusion as our father slipped into the kitchen. Time to check up on Mom. We found her surrounded by a clutch of keen readers over by the punchbowl.

"Hello, Francine. What a treat to meet an author. How many books have you written?"

"Could you tell us some of your titles? My grandkids love to read."

"I'm thinking of writing a story about my childhood pony. Can you help me get started?"

Our mother took her time answering. Her fanclub fell silent. It was like watching a talented surgeon scrub for surgery. We leaned in as she finally nodded and began speaking.

"What insightful questions. I cannot tell you how impressed I am by the lovely people I've met here on vacation. Truly. Now, speaking of children, our youngest got too much sun yesterday. I should ensure she's getting enough to drink. Do excuse me," she murmured before beetling off to find Dad.

I was delighted to take the fall for our premature departure.

CHAPTER 14

Madame Wasabi

"I'm really going to miss you, Kel," Mom observed quietly over our morning tea.

There were only two more weeks left in my FROG tenure. Back in May I would have been ecstatic but now I felt rather torn. The job had grown on me. I'd miss the familial chats with customers over coffee. They were akin to the cozy feeling one gets at Christmas, kicking back in pajamas and slippers, munching down on thick shortbread. It would feel weird to return to university where I'd be just one anonymous face among hundreds.

One thing I wouldn't miss was Francine's "Madame Wasabi" mode. Even though I'd grown up with this particular persona and all of its excessive enthusiasm, it still knocked me for a loop.

I selected the honorific as a nod to the authentic wasabi or Japanese horseradish whose pungent flavor fades after a mere 15 minutes, rather than the popular North American sushi condiment concocted from horseradish, mustard and green food coloring. For this particular trait of my dear mother's could be just as fleeting as the real paste. While gripped in this manic persona,

Francine focused solely on the trigger, rapturously extolling its virtues. But then, poof! The moment would pass and be forgotten. As her sales assistant, I found Madame Wasabi to be the most exhausting of my boss's personas, mainly because it usually fell to me to put out the fires it ignited.

The first FROG Madame Wasabi experience occurred during a visit to a local wholesaler in early August. I watched in alarm as the gentleman soaked up Francine's all-consuming adoration of an antique cinnabar lacquer Burmese temple offering box. It was not only pricey, but it had seen better days. Chipped, conical and hollow, it could have subbed as a colorful version of Hogwarts School of Witchcraft and Wizardry's sorting hat. This couldn't help but end badly. We'd either buy it and hang on to it forever or refuse it and crush the poor fellow's hopes.

Francine didn't agree. She brushed aside my reservations by begging to see more. As the wholesaler shot off into his inner sanctum, she showered me with droplets of joy. "We'll buy all he has. I've never seen *anything* like it. They'll fly out of the shop," the boss salivated.

Francine flitted about the tiny store searching out more unique delights, before finally honing in on a battered wooden Chinese physician's box. Costing more than I made in a month, its contents made me wince.

"Isn't it charming, Kel? We'll buy it, too."

Charming? No. "Harming" would be more accurate. The six sharp implements of various sizes were the stuff of nightmares, each one encrusted with ancient rust that looked like dried blood. We were now teetering ominously close to checkered mink dress land. Both this and the Burmese temple piece were too expensive, and I expected they'd take forever to sell. They'd only appeal to a rare few. I had to dissuade her before the fellow returned.

"I'm sorry, but I think it's just foolish to spend the big bucks on these, Mom. Why don't we go home and sleep on it? They're bound to be still here tomorrow."

To her credit, Madame Wasabi dialed down the enthusiasm a notch or two.

"We'll take these two," she declared. "You can tell him we'll sleep on the others."

Offloading the bad news delivery, she dreamily ran her fingers over the box's battered top.

The wholesaler produced an equally ugly Burmese twin and a smaller, distant cousin. My stomach clenched as Francine gaped at them in awe and the fellow danced on his tiptoes anticipating a large sale. When I mewled out an apology, explaining that our budget only allowed for two pieces at present, his eyes filled with disappointment. I felt for him but refused to budge.

In the end, both Francine and I were right. We purchased the other Burmese pieces a few days later and a major hotel chain soon snapped up all four. The physician's box proved to be a more difficult sell. It hung around for years, triggering countless Madame Wasabi episodes. My radar engaged each time the euphoric Francine thrust it upon unsuspecting customers. As she waxed on about its "medicinal powers," and wistfully pondered its provenance, I reassured the horrified observers that the tools were not actually drenched in blood but were simply rusty.

While the Madame Wasabi persona was challenging, I couldn't possibly imagine that it would be the key to forcing my hand on the leave-or-stay issue.

Francine and I spent the morning of the last Saturday in August rearranging the front window. As usual, it took much longer than anticipated. We had to completely rearrange the crowded shop as the old window pieces didn't fit in the space vacated by their replacements.

Francine slipped out "for a quick check in with Mrs. King," which was code for a restorative chat with her favorite salesperson at the nearby Edward Chapman's Clothing store. She wasn't gone five minutes before I spotted the two women peering in from the sidewalk. They seemed mesmerized by this week's window showstopper. Crafted out of a buttery, heavily grained *keyaki* wood (Japanese zelkova) with contrasting ornate metal handles, the mid-sized, two-piece Japanese clothing chest was a beauty. I smiled and waved, causing them to rush inside.

"What is it and is it affordable?" the taller one asked.

I adored them on the spot.

"Isn't it lovely? It's called a 'tansu', which is the Japanese word for a storage chest. This two-piecer was made to store clothing and dates from about 1860."

"How wonderful. Nice to meet you! I'm Beth and she's Susan. I have to say that we've never seen anything quite like it before. Tell us more," the shorter one enthused.

I clambered back into the window and swiveled the tansu toward them. "The locking mechanisms can be a clue as to a tansu's age. Generally, the more intricate they are, the older the piece. See this knob on the small door here? Watch what happens when I press on it."

I giggled in anticipation of their reaction to the two narrow drawers concealed behind the door. But when I pressed on the knob, it refused to budge.

"How odd. It opened for me just a few minutes ago. I can get it open with a paperclip. Do you guys have time?"

Susan leapt athletically onto the platform and dropped to her knees beside me. Beth grinned up at us as Susan propped her silver metal frame glasses high upon her forehead and peered at the locking mechanism.

"Just give her a second. Susan is a whiz at locks. We think she must have been a cat burglar in a previous life. She can open pretty much anything."

The amateur locksmith whipped out a tiny flashlight attached to her key ring and shone the light into the keyhole. I held my breath as she nudged the knob with her thumb and gave it a little tug. "I think an Allen key would do the trick. Do you have some?"

Unfortunately no.

"Okay, we'll go home and get ours."

Certain that I'd never see them again, I couldn't believe it when they returned just two hours later. I'd come to accept that most folks employing an exit strategy didn't actually come back. Damn. With Francine transporting a customer to Tolmie Street to view one of our nineteenth-century Japanese screens, I'd have to handle this alone.

Susan jangled onto the platform clutching a large metal ring laden with a formidable range of Allen keys. Beth and I hovered as she jiggled a key into the lock. Nothing budged. She selected a size or two up and tried again. We were treated to a subtle click. Susan broke into a smile and pressed on the knob. The tiny door flew open! It was magical. My mangled paperclip would have taken twice as long. The talented woman waved away my admiration.

"It's nothing. You just need the right tool. Maybe spray a little WD-40 into that keyhole and on the knob to loosen them up. I'm happy to help should it happen again."

"Oh, Susan, do look. These tiny drawers would be perfect for hiding your coins! And the bigger drawers open like butter sliding off a hot potato," Beth squealed with excitement.

I slipped away to let the newbies discover its wonders in peace. Their enthusiasm conjured up memories of Francine and Godfrey's first visit to The Lantern Shop years before. However, when the two waved me over a few minutes later, I steeled myself for bad news.

At an encouraging nod from Beth, Susan softly queried, "Is the $3,000 price firm?"

I didn't think. I simply shaved off 10 percent out of sheer gratitude. Not only had they saved the day regarding the lock, but they'd come back.

The couple stared at me in shock.

"$300 off? Are you sure? You won't be fired?"

"Nope, not a hope. My mom's the boss. I'll toss in the tidbit about your locksmithing skills, Susan, and she'll be won over."

Perhaps worried that I'd change my mind, they whipped off a check for the full amount and slapped down an excessive amount of identification. I felt a bit unsettled. After they each lugged a section out to their SUV and stowed them snugly into the back, they thanked me profusely. I should be thanking them! They'd just gifted me my largest sale to date.

Of course, Francine was delighted with the news and eager to meet the pair. She didn't have long to wait. I was wrapping up the sale of a Japanese antique hand mirror when they slipped quietly into the store a week later. My boss zipped over and the three were soon giggling like old friends.

"Oh, Kelly! Your mother is such a kindred spirit. We've cooked up something rather special, haven't we?" Beth beamed mischievously once I joined them.

My Madame Wasabi radar instantly engaged.

"Frankie is going into business with us!"

Pardon?

Francine's animated face left me aching for clarification. However, with all three twittering about like robins, the reveal was slower than thick ketchup. Susan was the first to note my frustration.

"It all started when your mom shared how she moved about so much as a girl. How incredible she attended nine different schools, 'eh?"

What did that have to do with the antique business?

"We truly connected over your mother's itchy feet," Beth added helpfully.

I was thoroughly confused.

"She's like us. Every two or three years Susan and I get a hankering to move. We nattered on about what we look for in different houses and the conversation flowed from there, didn't it?" The other two nodded blissfully. "When we discovered that we all share the same dream, well ... that's when it clicked." Beth paused, her eyes shining. This was torture. I silently urged her to rip off the damn Band-Aid and get on with it. "We're forming a home renovation business!"

This was a beaut. Even for my mother. Madame Wasabi was indeed fully locked and loaded. She gripped my hands.

"Oh, Kel. You were *so* right about these two. They're delightful. I could not have better partners. Just think of how far we'll go."

Beth clapped joyfully. "And guess what?"

I could only manage a vacant stare.

"I'm handing in my notice tomorrow."

Oh dear God.

Madame Wasabi had really done it this time.

My mother, who always handed off the simplest handyman tasks to someone else, had this sweet couple convinced that they were going into the home renovation business with her. Of course they did. No one was more persuasive than Francine in full-on Madame Wasabi mode. Toss in the fact that they'd just met her, they couldn't possibly understand that this idea was but a fleeting whim.

What was she thinking? Francine had a full-time business already and was about to lose her only sales assistant. She couldn't handle taking on anything more. Someone had to put the kibosh on this renovation concept and fast. I'd better choose my words carefully. It was imperative that Susan and Beth retain their good opinion of my boss as she truly meant them no harm.

"My goodness, what a truly enterprising idea. I love it." Everyone beamed. "However, I think we need to pump the brakes a wee bit, ladies. We've still got two more years on our lease here and if our top salesperson abandons me to work with you, well, FROG'll go bankrupt by Christmas. Of that I have *no* doubt."

While Beth and Susan's faces flooded with understandable confusion, Francine's shone.

"Kel. Are you saying that you're staying? You're *not* going back to school?"

I knew in that instant. I'd stay on at FROG for one more year. Someone had to save Francine from herself.

CHAPTER 15

Sales Tips 101

Now that I'd committed to stay on at FROG for one more year, the attitude shift was not unlike when a guest becomes a regular roommate and is expected to take on more of the chores. Francine's expectations of my sales efforts understandably ramped up. But she approached the topic with care.

"What's your biggest challenge here, Kel?"

That was easy. I dreaded one particularly "unique to antiques" sales question. That of the ubiquitous, "What's your best price?" It was crazy. You'd never ask for a better quote on a dozen eggs or whether you could get a discount on your bacon, yet it was common practice at FROG. When someone asked me that, I had absolutely no idea on how to respond other than awkwardly replying, "Let me check with Francine."

My mother nodded, pleased she had something to work with.

"Okay, we'll start with inventory pricing. Once you understand what's involved, I think you'll be able to answer the question yourself."

Francine produced the dreaded inventory book. The multiple columns with their baffling figures had always scared me. This was at least three years before we'd even consider a computer. As she slowly outlined the steps that determined a piece's retail price, it dawned on me it was similar to the pricing of the seniors' bus tours at my previous job. The final price included the original cost and all of the additional expenses associated with it. At FROG, the extras ranged from repairs to packaging, shipping, customs duties, and delivery. Encouraged by my surprising interest, Francine quickly moved on to the sticky "best price" issue.

"There is an art to it, Kel. Let's start with the basics. As a rule, you're pretty safe to initially come down 10 percent. However, if it's a designer or a special situation (don't worry you'll quickly develop a feeling for those) or if it's a loyal customer with a great payment track record, you can come down 15 percent. That's the Special Family Price. You've heard that term, right?"

I rolled my eyes. If I'd heard it once, I'd heard it a thousand times. I liked the name and the policy. Remarkably similar to the offers she made to genuine family members, it was more than a disingenuous sales gimmick.

Francine misinterpreted my reaction.

"Don't worry, this will all soon seem quite natural, Kel. Now, your toolbox contains another option. Can you guess what it is?"

I envisioned Francine negotiating with a customer and the answer came quickly.

"Yes! Suggesting that they take advantage of our 'Never, Never, Hardly Ever' payment plan."

"Excellent. If they decide to opt for it, remind the customer that if they give us post-dated checks or credit card slips, they can take their treasures home. Otherwise, we'll be happy to store them until the last payment is made."

With Francine now steepling her fingers and peering at me over her glasses, it was obvious we were just getting started.

"Selling is an art, Kel. I'm delighted to pass on what I've learned over the years." She leaned back in her chair and twirled a lock of hair around her finger. "It's important to remember that not everyone is blessed with imagination. I always study their faces. If they're frowning, it usually means they can't picture a piece in their home."

Not in my experience. It usually meant they were trying to figure out how to tell me they preferred to work with Francine. However, that tidbit could wait for another day. My mother wouldn't welcome any distraction. She was on a roll.

"As you well know, Kel, our pieces look so much better once they are removed from here and are allowed to shine on their own merit. So, if someone is dithering, you should propose they take the piece home on approval and live with it for a while."

We grinned remembering the Dr. Humbert rug experience.

"Okay. But what if someone just wants to gussy up their house for a party and then return it, saying that it didn't work? And what if they damage the piece?"

"Great questions, Kel. However, I don't actually mind if a piece is selected to smarten up a house party. Who knows? A guest may ask about the piece and then check us out. Of course, we don't want anything coming back damaged, but most folks are exceptionally careful when they take something home on approval." She paused to let that soak in.

"Now, one more thing and we'll call it a day. What's the first clue as to whether they're only interested in a party showstopper?"

I'd no idea. I was still pondering the hubris of someone pretending they owned something they didn't.

"It's the first-timer who comes in just before closing," she smiled patiently.

As Francine broke off to welcome a customer, I took a moment to marvel at her skill. You had to admire my mother. She'd learned the art of selling antiques all on her own.

CHAPTER 16

Money In, Money Out

My heart sank as a frazzled Francine tossed her purse onto the desk and sank wearily into a chair. Normally she skipped into the shop after a meeting with the bank manager.

"It was awful. Just awful." She leaned back and closed her eyes. "I've got to line up another meeting next week. He wants my accountant there, too. Apparently our bank loan isn't coming down fast enough."

I nodded, knowing little about the bank loan beyond its existence.

"There I was, all primed for the usual pleasantries when he suddenly brought up FROG's finances. I couldn't believe it. Could you go and get us tea, Kel, while I look up Paul's number? I've got a splitting headache."

Of course she did. Poor Francine. I raced off, happy to be able to do something useful.

"Treats, too, you are a dear, thank you." She bit gratefully into the blueberry-studded scone. "Paul can make the bank appointment next week. He suggested that Peter join us, as backup. He'll supply him with copies of the latest year-end statements to study beforehand." Francine swilled tea before continuing in a less shaky voice. "They're good friends. Apparently Peter was Paul's fraternity brother at UBC."

I liked the inclusion of Peter, my brother-in-law. He founded the successful charter bus company where I'd previously worked, before he was thirty, some eight years earlier. If anyone knew how to deal with bank managers, it was him. But it wouldn't be easy for our independent Francine to accept advice from her son-in-law. This was going to be tricky.

Peter was up to speed when we gathered two days later over a Tolmie Street breakfast of fried eggs, toast and bacon. Having analyzed Paul's year-end statements, he was now asking for the recent monthly statements as well as the company's Mission Statement. Francine confessed neither existed, nor would they. The resulting chilly standoff was a classic reenactment of *The Zax*, the iconic Dr. Seuss tale of two obstinate souls.

Dad and I exchanged furtive grins over our coffee; he was also wondering who'd win this round. When Francine blinked first and agreed to supply the items necessary for the creation of monthly statements, I understood why. She needed her son-in-law onside at the loan discussion. However, I winced at the capitulation, knowing it must have cost her a lot. I quickly offered to deliver the sales receipts, check stubs and bank deposits to Peter's bookkeeper.

The meeting with the bank manager went well. However, Peter came away with some chilling recommendations. He stressed the need for Francine to become familiar with the financial health of her business. She must hire a bookkeeper and be willing to continue the Tolmie Street breakfast meetings on a regular basis.

I anticipated yet more resistance from my boss, knowing it would be soul crushing to have someone poking about her business. However, she surprised me. Francine not only agreed to the breakfast meetings, but also went a step further by creating an informal advisory board consisting of Peter, accountant Paul, and her lawyer Bob. She also agreed to meet with Jane, Peter's bookkeeper.

I knew Jane well from my previous job. The reed-thin, highly competent blonde was more than capable of getting FROG's books in order, but I wondered if she had the necessary emotional stamina to handle our complicated Francine.

I was right to worry. Jane turned down Francine's offer of tea and an introductory chitchat in favor of "digging right in." More than a little annoyed, Francine hurled the requested sales receipts, bank deposits and checkbooks onto the office desk and joined me in the showroom, leaving the astonished bookkeeper to wade through the disorganized tangle alone.

My mother enjoyed a ten-minute reprieve.

"Shall I come out to you or would you be happier coming in here, Frankie?"

Francine looked at me in alarm; she couldn't do it alone. Feeling sorry for both women, I dragged two chairs into the office and we settled in on either side of Jane. Francine squirmed as the inquisition intensified, clearly interpreting it as an assault on her business acumen. Unfortunately, once again, I was unable to help. My knowledge of FROG's financials was limited to the recent intel regarding inventory pricing.

As the bookkeeper moved on to the accounts receivables, her astonished squeal could be heard out on the sidewalk.

"Is someone actually paying you over ten checks? That's nonsense. The payment stretches out to nearly an entire year, Frankie!"

Francine pinked up nicely and began proudly outlining the

pertinent details of the highly successful "Never, Never, Hardly Ever" payment plan. I braced for the bookkeeper's response.

"That makes no business sense whatsoever. You cannot let customers drag out their payments without any interest. I've never heard of such a thing. That policy must stop immediately, Frankie. Immediately," the woman finally managed.

Francine shot out of her chair like a breaching whale.

"No, Jane. Stop. Enough. The concept of the 'Never, Never, Hardly Ever' is *nonnegotiable*. It's how my husband and I began building our collection. It is what my customers deserve. No. Getting rid of that payment plan is not an option. It will remain."

As Francine flounced back down, all jutting chin and hunched shoulders, Jane slowly exhaled. She finally grasped the complexities of this gig.

No one spoke for a good minute. I was about to suggest restorative tea when Francine broke into a disconcerting Grinch-like smile.

"I won't work with you, Jane," my mother purred, sending a chill up my spine.

I couldn't believe it. Peter would be furious.

The bookkeeper floundered, first spluttering in righteous indignation, then flapping her spindly arms. However, Francine calmly held up a hand, effectively commanding rapt attention.

"No. I won't work with you, Jane," she reiterated, tugging confidently on her green and white Marimekko belt. "Kelly will. It's the perfect solution. She's keen to get more involved now that she's staying on for the year. I'll keep plugging away, making sales and turning over the inventory while you two sort out the financials' mess!" She nodded and rubbed her hands together decisively. "Excellent. We can iron out the details over a nice cup of tea. I'll be right back."

Francine swanned off to The Granville Diner, leaving me in quite the pickle. I had to somehow muster the courage to share an embarrassing secret. The words tumbled out in a garbled rush.

"I don't have a math brain. I'm hopeless. I failed Math 12, Jane, and had to retake it over the summer in order to get into university."

The bookkeeper studied me for a few seconds, before slowly nodding.

"Right. Let's just take it one sales slip at a time. It'll be fun."

The woman was delusional. But I wasn't worried. One word with Paul, and he'd kibosh the preposterous proposal.

But no. The accountant was not only thrilled with the update but he urged me to suggest lessons in bank reconciliations, too, whatever they were. I hung up, convinced we'd not advance past the first session. Faced with my inadequacies, Jane would understand the need to soldier through on her own. Or she'd quit and we'd simply get someone else to do the books.

Our initial lesson proved rocky. Jane found the incessant interruptions from Francine, random customers and the phone to be quite disruptive. She ended the session early, on the condition that I'd report to her tiny, sparsely decorated one-bedroom apartment on the following Tuesday night.

The bookkeeper surprised me; she was a good teacher. Over multiple cups of tea at her kitchen table, she patiently explained the reasoning behind each of her probing questions regarding the sales slips. My crippling anxiety slowly eased and was replaced, dare I admit it, by a fledgling curiosity. I agreed to a second lesson. The next Tuesday, we moved seamlessly on to accounts receivables, which left me thirsty for more. By the end of our third lesson, I found myself asking more questions than she. We were halfway through our fourth session when Jane uttered the inconceivable.

"You have all the makings of a natural bookkeeper, Kelly. But don't ask me how or why. Your dear mother is hopeless."

We'd *finally* hit on something I could shine at? Brilliant. Bring on the bank reconciliations!

Of course, this soaring confidence didn't last long. No, it vanished quicker than a mouthful of cotton candy the second Jane opened her door, squealing, "Let the serious work of bookkeeping begin, Kelly!"

As she fondled the spine of a skinny, blue hardback book, she reverently whispered, "Allow me to present The Ledger."

"I'm sorry. What is that?"

Jane sighed.

"The Ledger. It holds the key to the creation of a balance sheet and a profit and loss statement, Kelly."

The woman was talking utter gibberish.

"Relax, my girl, we're not talking calculus here. It's simply a book in which you track the acquiring and spending of money. Money in, money out."

My confusion eased as Jane patiently outlined the importance of weeding out our various expenses and earnings. I began to see how they could be accurately reflected on the profit and loss statement, which proved both illuminating and cringeworthy. The woman was nothing if not blunt.

"Now. About FROG's 'Slush Fund' account. What a holy nightmare. Am I correct in assuming that you and Frankie just dip into the 'Slush Fund' whenever you need a stamp, a coffee or a bite to eat?"

I swiped at the sweat beads blooming along my hairline.

"Your silence speaks volumes, Kelly. Right. First, the name. 'Slush Fund' implies inconsequential funds. From now on, I urge you to grant it the importance it deserves by referring to it as

Petty Cash. Going forward, you will accurately record each and every penny coming out of Petty Cash. At the end of the month, you will revisit these recordings and attribute them to the appropriate account. For example, stamp purchases will be noted under Office Supplies. Lunches recorded under Meals and coffee and teas under Snacks."

It was a lot to absorb. However, Jane's earnest stare necessitated a comment.

"Okay. Wow. That's quite the excessive recording."

She shook her head. I made a stab at a more appropriate response.

"So, at some point, you'll total them all up and you'll be able to tell exactly how much we wasted on random drinks and meals?" I babbled, doing my best to avoid those eyes. One glimpse and she'd instantly grasp the true depths of our profligate spending.

"Yes! Well done, Kelly. I also think it'll help Frankie rein in her spending."

Jane jabbed her index finger on the narrowest column in The Ledger pages.

"Now, please take particular note of this column. It's the salient one, where you record the cents. You'll appreciate it the first time you're out by a few pennies on the balance sheet."

"I'll be fussing over pennies? Surely not."

Jane sensibly closed the book.

As January rolled on into February, our bookkeeper shepherded me through the many steps leading to the creation of both the balance sheet and the profit and loss statement. It wasn't difficult, just time consuming. In those pre-computer days it meant hours of endless pencil jotting, and careful tallying on a cumbersome adding machine. I was hooked. The effort taught me the importance of knowing where FROG's money was being both acquired and spent.

Knowledge was power. I vowed to be much more responsible in the future. Poor Francine. She couldn't possibly have predicted this.

But that was nothing compared to the unexpected thunderbolt that was about to be unleashed.

After three months, I could read Jane pretty well. I knew something was afoot the minute she steered me away from the kitchen and into the pair of upholstered armchairs in the living room.

"Kelly, please hear me out before you say anything."

"Where'd I mess up, Jane?"

She frowned and waved her arms in a shooing motion. "Relax, it's nothing to do with you. It's me. I feel like I'm treading water here with all my friends happily married and raising children. I need to make some drastic changes." Her words tumbled out like spilled rice. "I've handed in my notice and given up this apartment. I'm flying home to London on the 21st."

No, that was impossible. Jane couldn't abandon us. And in just under two weeks!

"Who the hell is going to do our books, Jane?"

"Well, that's obvious. You! Just remember the four magical little words – 'Money in, money out' – and you'll be fine."

Well, hell. Wasn't that just peachy. My throat closed at the thought of my mother's reaction to the news that her fledgling sales assistant was being swapped in as her new bookkeeper. Jane would have to do that. I didn't think I could face it.

In the end, we told her together. My mentor beamed as I confidently reassured my boss, "It'll be fine, Francine. You'll see. As Jane always says, it's simply all about tracking how we acquire and spend the money. Money in, money out."

CHAPTER 17

You Want To Sell Your What?

Jane flew off to her new life, leaving the girl who failed Math 12 in charge of FROG's books. Was I scared? Surprisingly not. I felt a lightness, or an easing, knowing I could do something my boss couldn't. Looking back on my early days at FROG, it was as if we'd been seated assbackwards on a teeter-totter. As Francine routinely soared above, eager to leap to ever more achievements, I slouched far below, firmly tethered. However, just as my rash of sales provided some initial liftoff, these new bookkeeping skills cranked me somewhat higher. We weren't level but we were getting closer.

Francine appreciated my efforts. She patiently answered all my bookkeeping questions, only losing the plot when I struggled to balance the month-end numbers; my obsessive need to account for every penny left her lunging for her change purse.

"Oh for God's sake, Kelly, how much are you out? Three cents? Well, here, take these. It's just sheer tomfoolery to be spending hours fussing over such a paltry sum."

There wasn't any point explaining the futility of accepting those three pennies. She wouldn't get it. The only solution was to nod and dive back into my calculations. The error was in there somewhere.

A Vancouver interior designer soon hit us up with an interesting proposition regarding his vast collection of Asian antiques. For reasons we agreed to keep private, he wished to liquidate the lot through FROG on consignment anonymously. I liked the idea. Working on the books made me appreciate how consignment sales could be a rather sweet gig. Selling someone else's items cost us nothing.

When we popped over for a viewing, it was like parachuting into a gigantic FROG storage facility. Every conceivable Asian antique was on display, in multiples. Only fools wouldn't accept the lot, especially considering the majority were in immaculate condition. At a discrete nod from me, Francine laid out her terms.

"As you know, our shop is a quarter of the size of this warehouse. If you're willing to dole out the items on an as-needed basis, I think we can work something out."

The two sealed the deal with a handshake and settled on a commission rate of 10 percent, down from our standard 15 percent. We foolishly agreed to receive the first installment in 24 hours. After racing back to the shop, Francine began sorting out ballpark prices and I started drafting a promotional blurb to alert the troops of the impending windfall.

The response was immediate and positive, thanks to the quality, and in many cases, the rarity of the items. However, my thoughts on consignment pieces costing us nothing proved way off base. Pricing, placing and selling took the same amount of energy, regardless of the owner. Toss in the secrecy regarding the ownership, and Francine and I were soon quite exhausted. But we never betrayed his trust.

A few months later, we were approached by another person eager to sell a large collection on consignment. The circumstances couldn't be more different.

The gentleman hovering in our doorway had never been in before. He was unforgettable. In his mid-60s, he was awkwardly tall with arms that were much too long for his body. His nose protruded beak-like over a weak jaw, and combined with his thinning hair and slender build, he reminded me of a fledgling hawk. As we locked eyes, he flashed me an alarming grin.

"Hello, my dear. I need you."

While I currently didn't have anyone "special" in my life, he was not a potential candidate. I hesitated as he reached out a claw-like hand.

"Hi there. I'm Robert Sheldon. My dying mother is leaving me all of her stuff."

He delivered the words as if requesting butter with his toast. Impervious to my discomfort, he began whirling his arms and slowly spinning about.

"Your store looks just like her apartment," he said."It's crammed with crap like this."

A year into my employment at FROG, I automatically cringed at the phrasing.

"I need you to give me some idea of whether I'm sitting on a goldmine."

My jaw tightened. If the collection was huge, there was no way we could acquire the lot. The shop was already full to bursting; we'd recently restocked with the designer's pieces.

However, it was important not to get ahead of myself. This fellow wanted an appraisal and that was Francine's purview, not mine. A quick peek at our day journal revealed that the earliest opening was Tuesday morning before work. I penciled in the date and found myself asking whether Robert's mother would even appreciate an appraisal.

He sneered.

"Look, dear. Mother recommended that I come and see you! She only lives around the corner. Can't you pop by before Tuesday? If you can't, just give me the name of someone who can."

Aware that Francine would be annoyed if I botched this up, I somehow managed to bite back an angry retort and keep my voice low yet confident.

"No, I'm sorry. It has to be Tuesday, Robert. And you don't want anyone other than Frankie to do the appraisal. Few in the city know Asian antiques better than she."

"Damn." I sensed him shift gears as he twirled a bony finger around his limp bangs like overcooked spaghetti lumped on a fork.

"But surely you can make it later than 8:30 a.m.?" His syrupy wheedling only strengthened my resolve.

"No. We open the shop promptly at 10."

"Fine. I'll see you at dawn on Tuesday," he snapped and flounced out with neither a backward glance nor a thank you.

The habit of jotting down appointments and pertinent remarks in our day journal had now become second nature. Even though I could have spat out enough Robert Sheldon content to fill both pages, I recorded little other than a need for an appraisal of a dying mother's pieces. It was important that Francine not be colored by my opinion of Robert. I was also more than a little curious about which one of Francine's diverse personas would be triggered by the son's questionable attitude. This visit would be interesting.

When we walked into the apartment on Tuesday, Francine's eyes snapped open with delight. Even I could appreciate his mother's discerning taste. Her living room was draped in elegant antiques from all over the world; treasures every one. Nothing jarred as it could have in the hands of a less-gifted collector. The intricate ornamentation of the Louis XV chairs meshed nicely with the simple Chinese blackwood table and the plush, thickly knotted Moroccan rug. Several rich textiles, folded over the back of overly stuffed English sofas, blended seamlessly with the carefully chosen artwork; everything hinting at a life well and richly lived.

Francine was deeply moved. She slowly pivoted toward the hovering son and uttered in a voice thick with awe, "Your mother must be a very special woman."

"Yeah, I guess."

If Francine found his response distasteful, she hid it well. It was time to begin our assigned task. As she crept her way around the room, I followed alongside with my pen and paper, and Robert silently slipped into the kitchen where we soon heard him fussing with a kettle.

We worked as efficiently as possible, but the collection was so extensive we were only half done by the end of the allotted hour and 15 minutes. Robert rushed to join us when we slipped on our coats, his curiosity on full alert.

"So, ladies, am I going to be rich?"

Francine froze, her face a mask of disingenuous affability.

"Please thank your dear mother for allowing us the honor of viewing her collection. We've only just managed to get through half of it and ..."

"What! You're only half done? Aw, come on, give me an idea of what you think it's worth, would ya?"

His obtuseness proved to be the tipping point. It triggered the immediate transition into Francine's imperious I'll-show-you-the-proper-way-to-behave "Empress" persona, beginning with the subtle straightening of her spine and the slight raising of her chin. She then skewered him with a look most chilling.

"No, I'm sorry but that's impossible, Robert. I cannot *possibly* give you an accurate accounting until the entire appraisal is complete. Now, if you would be so kind, when would your mother like us to return?"

Robert gasped, as if Francine had suddenly begun speaking Italian. His eyes bulged as he exploded in rapid-fire beseechment. "Seriously? Didn't Kelly tell you that Mother is nearly dead? She won't care one way or the other. Look, I'm trying to get enough money together to finance my move to Thailand and I need to sell all this stuff to make that happen! I'm just waiting on you. Everything else is done and dusted."

Francine stiffened and I could just detect her whispered response.

"What a shame to break up this wonderful collection."

Finally grasping further entreaties were futile, Robert grudgingly agreed to reconvene at the same time tomorrow.

Francine hissed her opinion as his door closed behind us.

"I'm speechless, Kel. Speechless. He's impossible. He may be able to travel the world, but he hasn't a fraction of his mother's sensibilities. I do wish we could have met her."

CHAPTER 18

Symphony Phony

While my work life at FROG was offering some unexpected opportunities by the spring of '84, my personal life wasn't keeping up. Not by a long shot. It had tanked with the unfortunate departure of both of my best pals – Melinda to start her married life in Ontario and Margaret to return home to New Zealand.

In addition to personally feeling lonely and somewhat vulnerable, I also felt extremely sorry for one of our customers. Just nine months earlier, the fellow tragically lost his wife in a freak avalanche accident while on a mountaineering vacation.

We knew very little about Allan or his wife Edith, other than they were childless. It was heartbreaking when the grieving widower slunk into FROG a few Saturdays after the accident. In his mid-30s, he was a shell of his former self. As Francine dispatched me on a restorative "hot tea and something sweet" run, I overheard her kindly reassuring him he was always welcome at FROG and that he needn't feel pressured to talk or engage.

Allan blossomed under this nonjudgemental attention and

gradually became a genuine FROG regular. While I felt we got to know him much better over those intervening months, I wasn't remotely prepared when he pulled me aside one busy Saturday afternoon.

"Kelly, Edith and I enjoyed season tickets to the Vancouver Symphony and, well, I think I'm finally ready to go back. I'm wondering if you'd join me as my guest?"

I froze with dread. Allan honestly couldn't have asked anyone less worthy; I wasn't the least bit interested in classical music. However, a night out was a night out. And those deeply chocolate-brown eyes were finally twinkling with a bit of their old sparkle, so I accepted.

Francine was delighted and batted away my concerns.

"I think it's very kind of you. He'll be able to cross that 'first' off his list and you might even enjoy yourself."

The evening didn't begin well. I was crippled by the fixation that "Edith should be here." Everything reminded me of her. This was her seatbelt, her car, her husband. When we arrived at the theater, I was momentarily distracted by the location of our seats. Smack in the middle of the auditorium, they were blessed with impeccable sight lines. But as my host slumped down into his seat with a ragged sigh, I felt impelled to provide distraction.

"So, Allan, do you play?" I asked, my voice an octave higher than normal.

As he dragged confused eyes to mine and his mouth began to crumple, I blundered onward.

"Of course you play, what with all the hiking and shopping and antique collecting! Silly me. No, I mean do you play an instrument, Allan?"

I rushed to fill the awkward void.

"I played the piano and the flute for a few years when I was younger; both dreadfully. We inherited the piano from my grand-parents." Pausing for a much-needed breath, I was suddenly aware of the heightened curiosity from those seated nearby. His fellow season ticket holders were clearly wondering where Edith was. Dear God, they didn't *know*. Allan inched closer to the edge of his seat, ready to bolt. I began to giggle like a gossipy teenager.

"I really was a naughty girl, Allan. When I was in the fifth grade, I came up with an ingenious plan. I bribed my friend Annie with the promise of fistfuls of red licorice if she'd practice for me. She was one gifted pianist!"

I was now a fully fledged nightmare. Normally lauded for my ability to be a good listener, I was rendered incapable of silence. Allan's shocked inhalation could be heard five seats down.

"Francine was thrilled by 'my' stellar playing."

My host's coloring was now a pallid yellowy cream; not unlike that of an ancient piano keyboard, but that didn't stop me from blathering on.

"It took Francine days to figure out that it wasn't her darling Kelly plunking away."

Allan scrunched even lower in his seat. Perhaps he'd also spotted the smirking woman two seats down.

"I stopped playing the piano shortly afterwards ..."

The auditorium lights began to dim and Allan sighed with relief. Perhaps Francine would be invited next time. I certainly wouldn't.

CHAPTER 19

A Village-Worth of Brides' Jars

"Please don't be cross with me, Kel…"

We were deep into the fall of '84 and I should have been ensconced at UBC. But I wasn't. I was entrenched at FROG. I realize there should be a chapter devoted to a minute-by-minute breakdown of my glorious decision to stay beyond the year. But it wouldn't be authentic. I couldn't find any mention of a pronouncement in Francine's diaries and neither of us remember any hoopla surrounding the decision. I must have simply grown into the job; it clearly wasn't remarkable.

However, this phone call certainly was.

Francine's giggles bubbled down the phone line, kicking my inner bookkeeper into overdrive. The boss had been shopping. I couldn't believe it. Not two days ago, we agreed to concentrate on selling a chunk of the inventory before buying more.

"I've just stumbled across the most *amazing* collection of smalls for this Christmas."

Oh, she was good. What a perfect thing to say. Last year, we didn't have nearly enough smalls (our word for lower ticket items), and our pre-Christmas sales had been pretty dismal. FROG's trade picked up only after Boxing Day when folks dribbled in to buy something special for themselves.

Sensing an opening, her confidence surged.

"I popped in to see Stevie after work!"

My fledgling compliance evaporated. Without my steadying influence, Francine was incapable of resisting the sales skills of our favorite local wholesaler.

"The timing was perfect. He was just uncrating the first of his Chinese shipments and treated me to an early preview." She paused again, obviously considering what to reveal next.

"He unearthed the most amazing find in China."

Of course he did. My throat closed in anticipation of the impending financial damage.

"Stevie acquired a village-worth of brides' jars!"

Surely I'd misheard.

"Every single one has its original lid."

Now that tidbit grabbed my attention. I'd only ever seen ones with wooden replacement lids; the fragile ceramic originals shattered easily. Perhaps this wasn't so bad after all. Traditionally given to a bridal couple for use as storage of the once rare salt, oil, herbs and ginger, today folks coveted them for their hand-painted "double happiness" calligraphy symbolizing happiness, prosperity and fertility. Yes, I had to admit that a dozen or so of the reasonably priced blue-and-white wide-mouthed jars with their domed lids and bulbous bodies would be a welcome addition this close to Christmas.

My audible "hmmm" sent Francine plunging headfirst into Confident Frank mode.

"My timing was perfect, Kel. Stevie was fielding calls from dealers right across North America. Of course I snapped them all up!"

"How many did you buy, Francine?" I spat, saliva flying.

"All 80! Isn't that marvelous?"

Francine had spent God only knows how much on a gazillion brides' jars without even consulting me. My fingers grew numb clenching the receiver.

"What's the damage, Mother?"

"Now, don't go all funny on me, Kel. I knew you'd be upset if I spent the money all at once. I was very sensible." Her voice took on a tenor of extreme satisfaction. "Stevie not only gave me a very good price, but he agreed to three equal payments over time without interest."

Well, well. This was different. Prior to my signing on as FROG's bookkeeper, Francine would have merrily written a check for the full amount. I also had to admit that there were several advantages to snapping up all 80. It meant lower individual costs per jar and no competitive price war as we'd be the only Vancouver merchants selling them. Buying from the local honest dealer was also a boon. It eliminated the need to wait weeks for the shipment to arrive and then clear Customs.

I was about to ask where she planned to store this windfall, however, Confident Frank got there first.

"I've made all the arrangements for them to be delivered to Tolmie. We can store the bulk of them there. Stevie assures me they're all quite different. We can keep a dozen or so in the shop and bring out six at a time for folks to compare."

I liked that idea. It would be a nightmare to show dozens at once, especially for the ditherers.

However, Stevie kept one little secret from Francine. That of the arresting aroma. We were assaulted by it the second Godfrey pried open the first crate. I could almost taste the heady combination of earthy mold and sour vinegar. Ten jars, each wrapped individually in cardboard, were nestled tightly together on a bed of wet hay. Francine drew back, leaving me the task of plucking the first one out. I gingerly peeled back the sodden cardboard and recoiled. The pot was so encrusted with caked-on filth that it was impossible to make out any discernible color, let alone the hand-painted double happiness symbol.

"I'm sorry, love, but you're going to have to deal with this. I'm feeling a bit wheezy ... must be the hay." Francine managed, before she and Godfrey beetled upstairs, leaving me alone with the barnyard wonder.

I averted my head and held the jar under a rush of tepid water in my parents' massive laundry sink. Nothing remotely shifted. I reached for some bleach and poured a healthy amount onto a cloth and attacked the jar again. This resulted in a minute shifting of the grime. Time to call in the big guns. I filled the sink with scalding water, tipped in several more dollops of bleach and grabbed the industrial brush my father used to remove the sidewalk winter grunge. Several minutes of serious scrubbing allowed me to finally discern the steady hand of the craftsman. The effect of the cerulean blue pattern painted onto the white background was truly spectacular. Hope replaced horror.

The sparkling jars proved to be a hit. Each jar was indeed unique. Some were squat and bulbous and others cylindrical and lean, with the majority of them somewhere in between. While I gradually managed to get the cleaning process down to an efficient 15 minutes per jar, the actual experience never grew more pleasant. I still had to dart outside every few minutes to clear my head from the noxious fumes. The bleach also made my hands excessively slippery, which usually added an attentive five minutes to the drying and polishing.

"Oh, you're so lucky to have such a glamorous job," the young gal swooned as we eyed a lineup of jars one afternoon. She'd asked for assistance in selecting the perfect Christmas gift.

Glamorous? Unable to resist, I fanned out my hands for inspection. They were puffy, shiny and fiery red, as if I'd plunged them into hot wax.

"Oh my God. You should get those looked at. They're a mess!"

Her squeal brought the elderly Mrs. Shane, a retired teacher, tottering over for a peek.

"Glory be, dear. How many of those jars do you still have to bathe?" She asked, her face alight with concern.

"50," I bleated, watching her lips form a tight line.

"Two words, dear: 'Rubber gloves.'"

That and the hydrocortisone prescription worked miracles.

CHAPTER 20

Little Miss Spiteful

L est one has a notion that I was becoming a model employee these 16 months in, having taken on FROG's bookkeeping and grown more proficient at selling, rest assured – it couldn't be further from the truth. I still had a lot to work on. One of my many failings was a particularly cringeworthy personality trait best referred to as "Little Miss Spiteful." Although thankfully not nearly as prevalent as during the early months, she still tended to emerge every now and then alongside Francine's steamrolling Confident Frank and Mamasan Frankie. While in her clutches, I was a jealous bitch; snarky, taciturn and abominably rude to my boss. Today, armed with years of perspective, I suspect it was one of the perks of our working relationship.

One particularly memorable Little Miss Spiteful episode was triggered by the visit of Mr. Friday, an American executive sourcing unique furnishings for his newly renovated home. The two of us shared a companionable 15 minutes tootling about the shop before he spotted the exotic Thai Buddha cloaked in gold leaf and studded with colorful stones.

"You'd be perfect for the library," he opined under his breath before turning to me with a smile. "Do you ship to the States?"

"Yes, to all 50!" I gushed.

Francine suddenly scuttled over with the enthusiasm of a game show host. I watched, stunned, as she seamlessly closed not only the Buddha sale, but also an astonishing number of others. In just under 20 minutes, my boss racked up sales greater than the previous month's total. It was damned impressive. Did I bestow upon her the respect and joy that she deserved? Nope. I was seething with jealousy. Confident Frank had stolen Mr. Friday from me as efficiently as a hawk snatching a baby sparrow from its nest.

As the happy couple waltzed out the door for an impulsive gander at the treasures stored at Tolmie Street, Confident Frank finally remembered her assistant. She cooed, "We won't be long, Kelly, dear!" When my mother returned some two hours later, Little Miss Spiteful was locked and loaded.

"What a fun afternoon, Kel. It's so refreshing to work with someone who can make their mind up so quickly! Honestly, my head is just buzzing." She flounced into a chair. "Please call the packaging store. We've got a huge shipment heading to the States."

"Great." I growled maliciously.

The comment bounced off the ebullient woman like droplets on varnish.

"What an afternoon. After snapping up several of the smaller tansu at home, he swooned over the *kaidan* tansu (staircase or step chest) and then some of the beaded Thai wall hangings! I couldn't believe it. We were just leaving when he spotted that pile of rugs near the front door."

The man wasn't clairvoyant, Mother. They were stacked five feet high. He couldn't miss them.

"He bought the lot. How lucky I was working today."

So lucky.

Little Miss Spiteful vowed to get even.

When Mr. Friday called a few weeks later, Francine's face was transfixed with joy.

"He's returning to Vancouver and called to set up an early morning meeting here. Isn't that grand, Kel? I am looking forward to seeing him. We must remember to give him coffee and stock up on some of The Granville Diner's sticky buns."

What was she thinking? The trim fellow probably ate very little breakfast and likely only protein at that. However, enveloped in my Little Miss Spiteful cloak, I said nothing. Mr. Friday was officially Confident Frank's client, let her take care of him.

When I crawled in on the appointed day, Francine was in overdrive. The freshly waxed Chinese blackwood altar table boasted a substantial buffet offering. My parents' coffee pot took pride of place. An ancient and permanently stained affair, it delivered a robust two cups at best. Plunked alongside were three of Tolmie Street's best mugs, a gigantic Costco-sized tin of ground coffee, several crisp coffee filters, and a half-empty, four-liter plastic milk jug. Platters of The Granville Diner's thickly iced cinnamon buns and their chocolate chip oatmeal cookies completed the tableau. Good Lord. Confident Frank had prepped for an entire hockey team, complete with coaches and trainers.

This could be good.

Mr. Friday arrived promptly at 7. He wasn't alone. Sydney, his daughter, tall, blonde, and blessed with a toothy smile, glanced at the spread and blanched. My heart soared.

When Francine bustled forward, she just managed to stop herself from bowing.

"It's wonderful to see you again so soon, Don, and what an unexpected treat to meet your lovely daughter. Coffee's on. Who'd care for a cinnamon bun? And perhaps a cookie or two?"

The polite response of "just two black coffees, please" was positively mollifying and spurred me to not only dole out their coffee but also to attend to Francine's tea. I cared not a whit that my own caffeine hit would have to wait. Finally, after some awkward moments while everyone sipped their drinks and discussed the weather, Confident Frank rallied and began ushering the couple about the store with all the attributes of *Pride and Prejudice's* obsequious Mr. Collins.

After a good 20 minutes and a second freshly brewed cup, Mr. Friday shot a discreet peek at his watch. I found my curiosity matching Francine's, I couldn't help myself. What truckload of treasures was he going to buy today?

"That pillbox will be perfect for Mom, right, Sydney? If you could write it up, Frankie, we'll be on our way. Many thanks."

The good gentleman was referring to one of our miniscule sterling silver pillboxes equipped with an antique blue and white porcelain shard lid. It retailed for a whopping $50.

I still wonder if Francine had spent more on the breakfast repast. Kind daughter that I am, I've never asked.

CHAPTER 21

Back Issues

B y now, I fully embraced Francine's belief that we could
often learn more about our pieces from knowledgeable regulars. Today's lesson was particularly enlightening. Craig,
a textile whiz, and I were studying a 150-year-old red-and-white
silk Japanese wedding kimono. He was pointing out the unique
finesse of its creator when Francine suddenly hollered from the
door, "I'm just heading to the bank to make a deposit, Kel. I might
pop in on Mrs. King afterwards."

Mrs. King, a quiet, gentle soul in her mid-sixties with a puff
of carefully tended blond hair and an acute sartorial eye, was
Francine's go-to sales clerk at Edward Chapman's, the iconic
British women's clothing store situated just around the corner
on Granville Street. Francine was one of their best customers. Her
diaries are littered with mentions of retail therapy sessions there.

"Excellent. I hope she's forgiven you," I cheekily retorted.

"What was that about?" Craig asked, his curiosity sparked.

I debated as to whether I should share the story of Mrs. King's
unfortunate experience with FROG. However, Craig had been so

forthcoming with his kimono knowledge, I decided he'd appreciate being told.

I explained how Mrs. King had stopped in on her coffee break. It was her first visit to the shop and we were delighted when she went home with a charming antique Chinese porcelain plate. Mid-nineteenth century, it featured a large prancing blue and white horse.

Craig raised an eyebrow. "And that's a problem, because …?"

"Because she brought it back, just two days later."

Francine had rushed to put the obviously upset Mrs. King at ease.

"How was last night's dinner party, Margaret?"

The good woman managed to pull herself together.

"Thank you for remembering, dear. The party itself went very well. Everyone so admired the plate when I passed around the appetizers. I shared where I bought it and how kind you were to give me the special family price." Mrs. King frowned and closed her eyes. "After everyone went home, I gently lowered it into a sinkful of hot, soapy water to soak, just as you told me." The words now tumbled out. "I couldn't believe it! The lovely horse suddenly galloped off the plate and began swirling about in the water!"

"Oh, Kelly," Craig gasped.

"Exactly. But get this. When she gingerly withdrew it from our elegant navy blue and gold FROG merchandise bag, it could have been a different plate altogether. The horse had indeed bolted. Now sparkling surgical white, it looked just like those common restaurant platters that dish up today's fried chicken special. Of course, we refunded her in full."

"But what's the story on the design?"

"Turns out it was an image transfer applied after the glaze. So much for it being a unique hand-crafted nineteenth-century piece.

Yet another reminder to be very judicious with our purchases in the future."

As much as I liked Craig, I refrained from sharing my suspicions that the glorious awkwardness of Mr. Friday's recent breakfast visit probably provoked today's visit to Mrs. King.

However, when Francine finally returned, I felt nothing but remorse. My poor mother had aged a good 20 years in just under an hour.

"Something dreadful has happened, Kelly," she croaked. I reached out as she grimaced, visibly gathering the strength to speak.

"I was perfectly fine ten minutes ago. Completely normal. I had a lovely chat with Mrs. King, but when I stepped onto Granville Street, liquid fire suddenly shot throughout my lower back and down the outside of my right leg. I think I'm going to throw up."

I began to prattle.

"But that's impossible. You were absolutely fine when you left, Mom! Did you have a stroke? Are you sure you didn't fall or get pushed or something?"

"No. It's the strangest damn thing. This pain is pure torture. I can't sit or stand. I need to walk."

And walk she did, for the next half hour. Round and round and round the shop. It was too much. We'd both be better off if she went home.

"Why don't you go get some heat on it, Francine? I'm sure you'll be back on your feet tomorrow," I soothed.

Dutiful daughter that I am, I confess I gave it no more thought until Francine woke me at 7 a.m. to report that the shooting pain had migrated down into her toes overnight.

"I don't think I got a wink of sleep, Kel. I won't be in today. I've got an appointment with a back specialist this morning. Dad suggested it."

Whoa. Our Godfrey routinely prescribed "a stiff gin and tonic" for the family's various ailments. This was a serious upgrade.

I was deep in the weeds of the December financials when the boss finally reported in later that afternoon. Distracted, I foolishly asked, "Are you all better now?"

Her response was delivered in an oddly brittle voice, as if chowing down on a mouthful of glass shards. "I cannot begin to tell you what I've been through these past few hours, Kelly. It was an unmitigated hell, a purgatory beyond anything you can imagine."

She rebuffed my pathetic attempts to back-pedal.

"I need you to just listen and not speak. Can you do that? Thank you." Francine drew in a long, shaky breath. "Your father insisted that walking the dog took priority over driving me to the appointment. I tried to drive myself but when I couldn't even swing one leg in the car ..." She fell silent for a beat before wobbling on. "I was forced ... to call a taxi."

My mother had my whole attention now. Just as we weren't a Q-tips or rubber gloves family, we also weren't a taxicab family. It wouldn't occur to us. We'd either get a ride from a family member or walk.

"When the monstrous vehicle pulled into the driveway, it took me a full ten minutes to get to it. It's for the disabled, apparently. However, I don't believe that. The driver didn't offer me a wink of help. He didn't even get out."

I imagined a huge black cab, like the finest in London.

"I got such a shock when I finally wrenched the passenger door open. The entire back seat was slashed to ribbons. It was one big massive explosion of orange colored foam innards. What? Stop laughing. Honestly, Kelly, it was absolutely dreadful. I shut my eyes and tried to sit but that was impossible. My leg and lower back just screamed in pain. Finally, after a series of excruciatingly painful attempts, I finally discovered the only comfortable position was full frontal. Picture it. Me, stretched out on my tummy, with my face smashed down into the filthy foam."

I burst out laughing yet again. Thankfully so did she.

"Oh, it gets better, Kelly, let me tell you. After enduring the 20-minute ride with my nose buried in the depths of the disgusting foam, we finally arrived at the medical building. I had the driver fish out the money and he probably robbed me blind." She stopped to let that concept soak in.

"I nodded at the elderly woman shuffling alongside me to the elevator, acknowledging her similar distress. It turned out that we were visiting the same doctor. You should have seen us hobbling up to the front desk. Despite our assertions that it was physically impossible, the perky young receptionist kept urging us to sit. She's clearly *never* had a back problem."

"And what did the doc say about yours, Mom?" I asked, hoping to speed things along.

She treated me to a long reproachful pause, before continuing in a barely audible whisper.

"The man appraised me for all of five seconds before proclaiming, 'If I'd known you were in this much pain, I'd have made a house call. You've got sciatica and should be in bed.' He scribbled out a pain meds prescription and advised me to return if it's not better in two weeks. He then muttered some nonsense about potential surgery. That was it. There was no removal of clothes, no questions, nothing. I'm furious. To think I went all the way down there in that taxi from hell, and ..." her voice trailed away. I didn't dare ask how she got home.

In the end, the sciatica was deemed to be nonsurgical, however the recovery was lengthy. It struck on the 23rd of January and it wasn't until February 16th that she was able to work a full day.

According to her journal entries, Francine spent the majority of her time darning Godfrey's socks. By the end of a week and a half she'd already darned 22 pairs, leaving me wondering exactly how many pairs my father actually owned.

In the big picture, her timing was good. This was my first lengthy period of working solo. I shudder to think about this happening in the early months of my employment. It could well have resulted in the termination of FROG.

CHAPTER 22

Tea for Three

W
e were back to full staffing in March and it was unusually quiet. A day where no one comes into an antique shop is a challenge, a string of two or three days in a row is soul-sucking. Francine and I had exhausted our "Who Am I" game options and were desultorily dusting when a plump, disheveled woman in her 70s tentatively popped her head in. I summoned a smile as Francine darted toward the door.

"Welcome, you've come at the perfect time. I'm just zipping out for hot drinks. Would you prefer coffee or tea?"

The greeting could not be more effusive.

"Um. Tea? I guess? Just let me just get you some money."

"Nonsense. It's our treat. I'll leave you in Kelly's capable hands," Francine burbled before dashing out.

The customer wasn't the only one spinning with confusion. This would actually be our second tea run in under 30 minutes. This stranger must be super special. As the woman sank gratefully into a chair, I scrabbled for connection.

"So, when were you last in?"

She managed a weary smile.

"Never, dear. This is my first time. Several of my friends have mentioned your store."

"Well, welcome. I'm Kelly, Frankie's daughter. We're a mother-and-daughter team." A few months shy of two years at FROG, I didn't think twice about admitting I was Francine's daughter. It eased the nerves of the first timers.

"I'm Mrs. Park and please excuse my appearance. I've just walked all the way from Granville Island. I'd forgotten how steep that hill is ..." Her complexion paled as she leaned back and closed her eyes, causing me to dearly hope that Francine wouldn't be gone too long. This was growing more awkward by the second.

When the boss bustled back ten minutes later, I clamped a forefinger to my lips. Mrs. Park was now sound asleep. Francine tiptoed into the office to lose her jacket and the customer stirred.

"Oh, goodness, I am sorry ..." Mrs. Park cried, swiping at her eyes.

"Please don't worry. I fall asleep here all the time. It's something to do with the air," my mother breezily fibbed. I bit back a smile as Francine brandished a thick date square. "You simply must have one, dear. They're famous on South Granville."

The three of us tucked into the robust squares. Thankfully, the refreshments soon worked their magic. Mrs. Park pinked up nicely and after brushing away a few wayward crumbs, sighed happily.

"Folks could certainly learn from you, Frankie. Do you two have time for a story?"

We had nothing but.

We nodded and perched on the edge of our chairs like children eager for a treat.

"It's about getting a new car. My old one died last month. I did my homework and when I finally settled on a certain Mercedes model, I dropped by the local dealership to check it out. Three youthful salesmen were standing about chatting. I strolled over and waited for them to notice me. Not one did. They kept chatting about the previous night's hockey game."

Francine's gasp mirrored my own.

"It was as if I was invisible. Granted, I was dressed somewhat similar to today, except maybe with better footwear."

She caught us shooting discrete looks at her feet, and grinned. We could easily make out a pink varnished nail through the hole in one of her shoes.

"They clearly dismissed me as a nonstarter. I wasn't having that. I located the model on my own and slid into the front seat. I played with the lights, the mirror and the seats; just stopping short of tooting the horn. It was a beautiful car, even better than I imagined." She paused to drain the last of her tea. "However, short of driving it off the lot, nothing could get the attention of those three clowns. I gave up and waltzed into the Volvo dealership next door."

"Good for you, Mrs. Park. I'd have done the same," Francine aptly noted.

"As you should, Frankie. Being older shouldn't make us invisible. I'm happy to say that it was a completely different situation next door. I explained my situation to a nice young fellow, who listened carefully and asked me a few questions. He then led me over to a snappy-looking white number. I fell in love with the vehicle on the spot."

"Did you get a favorable payment plan?" I had to know.

"No, dear." She winked at me. "I paid cash."

Oh, if the Mercedes boys only knew ...

Mrs. Park stretched, and stood up.

"I need your help today, ladies. I'm looking for something that

I can hide my stereo in, preferably something that's both practical and beautiful."

After viewing several potential options, Mrs. Park admitted she liked the look of the exquisite nineteenth-century two-doored Chinese blackwood cabinet. The woman listened patiently as Francine outlined the NNHE payment option.

"Thank you, dear. That is most considerate. However, I'll pay the $3,000 in cash."

Mrs. Park had a new treasure and FROG had a new loyal friend. I confessed to Francine that both women had taught me a huge lesson regarding the importance of ensuring everyone felt welcome, regardless of age, appearance, and gender.

"I'm glad, Kel. We wouldn't want you to be lumped in with the Mercedes boys."

CHAPTER 23

You Gotta Take the Sour with the Sweet

Okay, I wasn't perfect. It was one thing to slap on my welcome face, it was quite another to genuinely warm up to some folks.

Robert Sheldon certainly didn't improve upon further acquaintance. Whenever we met, there was always an undercurrent of insensitivity. The oft repeated, "I'm gloriously free now that Mother has finally died," trumped everything.

Our relationship promised to be a long one. Robert stressed the importance of making him "as much money as possible" before he flew off to a new life in Bangkok. He insisted on personally collecting any future checks whenever he "reluctantly flew back to Vancouver." We weren't to mail them.

We met another unique character around this same time. A year or two younger than me, Amy waltzed in and snapped up a small contemporary Chinese silk four-panel screen and two end-table-sized nineteenth-century Chinese blackwood tables in just under five minutes. It took me longer to wash my dishes and I lived alone.

Thoroughly embracing the Never, Never, Hardly Ever payment plan, Amy plunked down a cash deposit of $225 and gave us the remaining balance in 10 post-dated checks of $75 each, stretching into late December. Lord knows why we agreed to this.

Francine dutifully filed the checks away as I schlepped the three items out to Amy's car, a late '70s dark green AMC Gremlin.

"Put the screen in the trunk and the tables into the middle, Kelly. Don't worry about the crap. Just shove it aside," Amy directed, leaving me to orchestrate the awkward maneuvering between the piles of fast food wrappers and disposable cups.

I couldn't shake the feeling that something was a bit off. The visit had been blisteringly quick, especially for a newbie. Amy was also a gal of little words. She offered up none of the usual tidbits about jobs, interests, friends, partners or family. However, Francine wasn't concerned. She cautioned me about being overwhelmingly judgmental and noted that perhaps Amy was simply very private.

The first of her checks bounced. We weren't too concerned. Others had also simply forgotten to transfer the funds into the pertinent account. I called her at home and Amy picked up on the first ring. She promised, without a hint of regret or embarrassment, to drop a replacement check in the mail that very afternoon.

However, when that check failed to arrive, my second phone call received a terser response.

"Popping in to see you today."

Click.

When there proved to be no popping, I deposited the second of her post-dated checks out of sheer spite. Unfortunately, it also bounced back with an anonymous, angry red "NSF" scrawled across the front.

"Time to take control, Kel. We'll drop in on her before work this Saturday," the annoyed Francine declared.

Amy's apartment turned out to be just ten minutes from the shop, on the main floor of a lovely old house in the heart of the leafy residential Kitsilano. Francine rapped on the door and rang the bell. I inexplicably kneeled down to peer through the mail slot.

"Twweeeeeeeeee!"

A shrill ear-splitting whistle slammed through the flap, damn near deafening me. Francine, standing a few feet back, was thoroughly confused.

"Was that a bird, Kel?"

"If so, it's either flying about loose or the cage is right near the door, Mom. Maybe she's unable to hear us because of the screeching?"

We hovered about on the front porch alternating between ringing the doorbell and pounding on the door, all to no avail.

When we returned the following Saturday, a sleepy Amy immediately opened the door. Sporting a pair of red and white plaid flannel pajamas, she yawned and desultorily fluffed up her hair.

"Oh. It's you. I was coming to see you today."

Francine nodded coldly and pushed her way into the tiny front hall. I scrambled after, on high alert for any swooping angry birds. The spacious living room doubled as a disorganized storage locker. Crammed with furniture, there were heaps of clothes strewn over chairs and couches, discarded papers crunched up in balls on the floor and piles of dirty dishes on a tiny formica table. Our four-panel screen, spread out flat on the wall above the large television, was the only calming influence.

My mother barreled further into the room. I watched in amazement as she swept clothes onto the floor and snatched up one of the blackwood tables. After hurling it into my arms, Francine whirled around to face Amy.

"You'll get it back once you give us some cash."

Francine was magnificent. I was so proud of her. But Amy's reaction made my spine tingle. She giggled as if she'd been praised.

"That's fair. I'll be in next Saturday."

But of course she wasn't. When we returned, some two weeks later, we were met by a heavyset fellow dressed in a checked shirt and faded overalls.

"If you're looking for Amy, you won't find her. She and her husband blew out of here a week and a half ago, stiffing me out of two months rent. There's nothing left. They took everything."

After grappling with the novel husband concept, my thoughts turned to the poor landlord. Our financial situation seemed paltry in return. Thanks to Francine's quick thinking, we were out $500, not $750. However, I was curious about one thing.

"Did she have a bird?" I queried.

The landlord looked at me in confusion.

"No, she definitely did not. I don't allow pets. I routinely check up on everyone to ensure they don't try and slip one in."

I immediately pictured Amy or her elusive spouse supine on the floor below the mail slot, a pea-whistle clenched in their teeth. Utter madness.

We arrived at the shop to find Julia James waiting patiently outside. What a godsend. The woman was a literal ray of sunshine today, dressed in her brilliant yellow slicker and matching rain boots. Both Francine and I adored her. Born in Germany, she moved to Canada in her 20s, became an international flight attendant and wed a high-profile yet humble Vancouver lawyer. Always upbeat, she entertained us with tales of the treasures she picked up on her latest flight to Shanghai, Tokyo or another exotic city. There was never any mean spiritedness or gossip about her, just a genuine positivity. As per usual, she got straight to the point.

"Good Morning, Frankie and Kelly. I need a planter for my spring bulbs. Do you have any hibachis? I'd love a round wooden one. But a round blue and white number would also work."

Francine and I smiled at the color reference. Julia was a huge fan of blue and white. She'd purchased several of FROG's legendary brides' jars, both for herself and as gifts for others.

"We don't have any wooden ones. However, aren't there some blue and white ones in Mrs. Sheldon's collection, Kel?"

Julia cheerfully volunteered to help me look and we quickly unearthed two. After ten minutes of careful comparison, Julia chose the largest one and whipped out her checkbook.

"I can't forget today's date. It's my birthday!" She ran her hands lovingly over the glistening blue and white exterior. "This is the perfect gift from my husband."

Francine immediately offered to lower the price, but Julia wouldn't hear of it.

"Nonsense, Frankie. You are selling it on consignment, and at this low price, I'm sure you aren't getting much out of the deal to begin with. I'm paying for it in full."

The kind soul even insisted on lugging it out to the car by herself. What an absolute tonic.

CHAPTER 24

Buying Solo

Francine received some sad news not long after Julia's birthday. Bard, her 80-year-old, larger-than-life mentor, had been diagnosed with terminal cancer and was closing down The Lantern Shop. However, when he offered my mother the opportunity for first refusal on every stick of inventory as a "nod to their 16-year friendship," Francine's reaction was rather unexpected.

Concerned that she'd be too susceptible to Bard's masterful sales techniques, she asked me to go as her proxy. When I spluttered my dissent, Francine quietly insisted that my newly acquired bookkeeping knowledge would curtail any overspending. I wasn't convinced. I might be able to price the odd antique now, but I seriously doubted I had the chops to purchase any on my own. Toss both Bard and Bette into the mix and her decision was beyond absurd. The wily couple wouldn't hesitate to steamroll me into buying potentially unworthy items.

But Francine persuaded me we could come up with a solid plan to ensure that didn't happen.

"You'll win them over Kel. I think you'll quite enjoy yourself." Of that, I was highly doubtful. My memories were of the duty visits to their home as a teenager; very dull affairs indeed. The childless couple had no interest in children. While our parents enjoyed endless gin and tonics inside, among the precious eighteenth-and nineteenth-century Asian antiques, Mike, Wendy and I were dispatched to their narrow lanai along with the barbecue and a wicker settee. We'd get hopped up on sodas and bowlfuls of Bette's delicious Chex Mix, a salty/garlicky concoction of cereals, mini pretzels, and mixed nuts. The spectacular view overlooking Honolulu quickly grew tiresome, leaving us bored and bickering.

Our hosts always underestimated time. "Dinner in an hour" inevitably stretched out to at least four; we were lucky if we ate before 10 p.m. Bard was in charge of the meat, either a hefty turkey or roast, which he always cooked on the barbecue spit. He'd dab on some sauce, flash us a disingenuous smile and bolt back inside.

I remember one particularly noteworthy sunset. Bard was impressed and he bellowed for our mother to come and see it. Now. It was as if no one else existed. Francine, engaged in a sensitive conversation with Bette, ignored his summons and by the time she deigned to look, the magic had passed. Bard fell into a sulk and made a big show of stomping off, seeking the comfort of Freya, his loyal German Shepherd.

He stumbled back just minutes later, pasty white. The dog was missing. When Godfrey calmly swept the premises and confirmed that Freya had indeed taken a runner, my siblings and I were more jealous than concerned. The lucky girl was free! Bard insisted that the men form a search party and my brother leapt at the chance to tootle about in our host's Cadillac. They scoured the neighborhood, but clever Freya was well and truly hiding.

Dinner was finally dished up at around 11 p.m. Everyone tucked in except Bard, who cut a disconsolate figure at the head of the table.

"I can't eat, knowing that my precious girl is out there all alone," he muttered, shoving his untouched plate off to the side.

Everyone kept silent, except for his wife, who was dreamily dispensing the dessert. I dreaded Bette's desserts. She tended to use a liberal hand with the booze, which I didn't appreciate at 14. Tonight's specialty was some exotic ice cream topped with cognac-soaked pineapple chunks, dished up in the ubiquitous antique Japanese black and red lacquer square-shaped bowls.

"Oh my god! I've just had a vision of Freya," Bard blurted. "She's lying lifeless at the side of the road!"

Always proud of his "second sight," his mood blackened further and we left soon afterward.

We were awakened at dawn by Bard's ecstatic phone call. His girl had found her way home! Unharmed but starving, she was currently wolfing down his untouched dinner. I prayed she'd be spared the dessert.

Next year's festive repast was markedly different. With Freya firmly locked up in a back bedroom, Bette dished up a delicious kielbasa and bean soup in a shockingly timely fashion. However, when Francine perkily requested the recipe, Wendy, Mike and I rolled our eyes. We'd be dining nightly on that damn soup for weeks. Our mother had a lifelong disinterest in meal preparation and was inordinately proud of the fact that she "failed cooking." Whenever she stumbled across something we all liked, it became a firm fixture. When we complained, she'd switch it up and produce her favorite fallback: gems we referred to as "hockey pucks." These were hamburger patties grilled until blackened, and slapped between two slices of dry white bread. Yum. Little wonder I loved eating out at my friends' houses.

However, Francine's kielbasa and bean soup actually ended up being quite different from Bette's. She couldn't find kielbasa at our local Safeway and she couldn't be bothered to soak the dried garbanzo beans. Her solution? Boiled hot dogs and canned pork and beans. The leftovers were discreetly pitched and the recipe deleted from the roster.

When the boss confirmed my arrival and departure dates with Bard, she was surprised to learn he was still upset that his protege had been swapped out for her assistant.

"I assured him that you were more than capable of making informed purchases on my behalf, Kel, but he didn't sound terribly convinced."

Of course he didn't. The man still thought of me as the shy schoolgirl of 15 years ago.

I struggled to summon the courage to contact the couple on the appointed day. My main concern, apart from feeling like an absolute fraudster, was whether I should address Bard's health over the phone or ignore it until we were together.

Bette answered, thankfully. We engaged in some awkward pleasantries before she kindly invited me to "puu puus" and cocktails at their house followed by dinner at The Pacific Club. What a relief. Handfuls of Bette's Chex Mix, a stiff drink and a decent meal would set the perfect tone for our reunion much better than a sober meetup at The Lantern Shop.

Of course, my positivity vanished the second the taxi pulled up to their house. This was all wrong; my mother should be here, not me. I was an imposter simply playing the part of an antiques aficionado. To my horror, Bard yanked the door open before I could pull myself together. I was a mess and he looked … normal. Moreover, he did a masterful job of hiding his shock that this guest was no longer a gawky teenager.

"Come in, my dear. Bette's in the kitchen."

Traces of his wife's signature White Shoulders perfume wafted evocatively ahead of me as I trailed Bard down the long hallway toward the back of the house. My hostess, as plump and powdered as ever, arose elegantly up from her chair and after enfolding me in a surprisingly warm embrace, pressed a sweating glass into my hand.

"Help yourself to puu puus, dear," Bard bellowed, gesturing toward the plastic container of store-bought jalapeno dip nestled within a mound of Bugles corn chips. Rather than ask after his health, I cowardly opted for Bette's.

"Thank you for asking, dear. I'm very well. We're so delighted that The Lantern Shop will live on at your mother's store," she responded, solidifying my suspicions that I'd been dealt a very tricky hand.

I gulped down the fiery liquid. As it coursed to my toes, I suddenly recalled Godfrey's warning about this couple's drinks having the potency of "pure rocket fuel," and lowered the glass onto the shiny black table. I'd pace myself.

But something odd was happening to the table's surface. It was shimmying. A white circular band slowly expanded outwards around the base of my glass, much like the receding water in the early stages of a tsunami.

Sweet Jesus. The table was actually *white*. The solid black surface was an illusion created by cockroaches. My glass disturbed them. In my world, one cockroach was distressing, thousands were the stuff of nightmares. It took everything I had not to bolt, shrieking from the room.

I snatched up the glass and guzzled. Only then did I spot the stacks upon stacks of rectangular-shaped cardboard boxes peeking out from underneath the wooden kitchen cabinets. Cockroach deathtraps. I erupted into a series of audible gasps and shudders, causing Bette to giggle and gently pat my hand.

"Don't worry, dear. We recently treated the kitchen for a small cockroach infestation. Those roach motels are there to catch the random survivor."

"The random survivor?" Every box overflowed with crispy carcasses. I peeked over at Bard to see if he was as equally appalled, and my throat closed. The octogenarian was blissfully unaware that he was about to commit murder upon a fat and vigorous roach dangling from the tip of his bugle.

"Stop!" I squealed.

But it was too late. His mouth now full of crunchy goodness, Bard contentedly smacked his lips and cheerfully suggested a top up. I downed that fiery godsend in a trice.

"I'll just fetch our keys and you can drive us to the club, Kelly, dear." Bette drifted off, leaving me gobsmacked. These two were trusting me with their precious Cadillac after a pair of guzzled double-strength gin and tonics? I was about to insist upon a taxi when Bard suddenly plowed a finger through the dip and raised it to his lips. His failure to notice the pair of healthy roaches wallowing in the depths rendered me well and truly sober.

After successfully navigating the narrow, twisting streets of their neighborhood, I delivered us safely to the historic club located on the shores of Waikiki, just as the setting sun hovered mere inches above the horizon.

"Look out for the green flash, everyone!" Bard hollered as we approached our table.

I privately scoffed. I'd never experienced that natural phenomenon and was quite certain it was a myth. However, best not to upset my host. I glanced at the horizon as a brilliant flash of green suddenly shimmered over the tip of the golden orb as it sank into the ocean. Incredible. The evening went from strength to strength from then on. Bard and Bette could not have been more gracious. They were curious about Godfrey and Francine and even inquired after Wendy and Mike. They encouraged me to order whatever I wished and Bard ensured that our drinks were well tended. It wasn't until dessert that we touched briefly on his illness and he nudged the conversation toward his hopes for the inventory.

"You can sleep in tomorrow, dear. No need to rush over. As I'm sure your mother told you, she can have the lot. I'll give her very special prices on everything."

The elderly couple suddenly looked exhausted. It was time to go. But there was no way that I'd slide back into the driver's seat. I'd had far too much to drink. When they sensibly opted for a taxi, we hugged as family and I walked the short distance to my hotel, fully confident that I'd be able to navigate whatever issue arose tomorrow.

Of course, my attitude changed the moment I walked into the elegant and spacious store. This was crunch time. I was about to reveal FROG's carefully crafted game plan. The words tumbled out much harsher than I intended.

"Mom's issued me strict guidelines, Bard. I'm to assemble a list of the pieces that I think she'd like and will get back to you with her decisions tomorrow," I barked, and then forced myself to stop talking, mercifully remembering Mom's advice on the importance of keeping my brief short and to the point.

Bard sneered, his upper lip curling in distaste.

"Tomorrow? That's ridiculous. We'll settle it today, dear."

I willed myself not to apologize or buckle.

"That's impossible, Bard. Mom has become somewhat more judicious with her purchases now folks are no longer able to write off their antiques come tax time." The fellow glared at me and I plowed on, "Only pieces created by living Canadian artists can be written off. You can understand how that would have a huge impact on her sales."

Francine and I had grown a little suspicious of Bard's concerted push for FROG to snap up his merchandise. Although ill, he was in remission and now professed to have no definite closure date. Surely there were dealers in Honolulu that he could also call upon. Did he see her as a soft touch? It was important that I tread very carefully here and make smart choices for FROG. The tax issue was a ruse to buy us some time. Its success hinged on the American's ignorance of Canadian tax laws; this particular one was now over two years old.

Bard studied me appraisingly. When his eyes finally clicked internally, I braced. A decision had been made.

"Okay. If that's how Frankie wants it. Fine."

We'd cleared the first hurdle. I eagerly scanned the showroom as Bard slipped reluctantly into his office. While there were some stunning late eighteenth-century Chinese tables, cabinets and chairs and some lesser quality Korean chests in the mix, the majority of the pieces were Japanese. I zeroed in on the tansu, lacquered temple pieces, a handful of bronze birds, a few exquisite obis, some scrolls and several screens. I made careful notes of the pieces I liked and the ones I thought might be of interest to certain customers. The exercise took the good part of two-and-a-half hours and when I announced I was finally finished, Bard leapt up with the agility of a man 20 years younger.

"Okay, dear, show me your notes."

Crunch time. Waves of insecurity stole through me as the seasoned salesman began to peruse my list.

"You've not written down any of the Korean pieces," he snapped.

No, their joinery looked suspiciously new to me but I couldn't tell him that. He'd bristle at any authenticity queries. I blushed and scrambled for a plausible excuse.

"We're overloaded with Korean pieces at present and have more consignment ones waiting in the wings."

"Hmph. What's with all the notes about the screens?"

"I need to be able to carefully describe them to Mom. They're strictly her purview. "

"Only them? Surely you're not qualified to do all of the others ..." His voice fell away, underlining the true intent.

It was vital I stay calm. I might not possess one-tenth of his knowledge but at least I wasn't a raw recruit. As he continued to pick apart my list, the need for reinforcement grew stronger. I found myself calling upon my survival of last night's cockroach infestation.

He put down the papers and shook his head.

"Well, I must say I am disappointed. Good luck telling your mother, dear," he smirked.

I was dismissed.

I fled back to my hotel room and immediately called Francine. She listened attentively.

"Those last two screens are too expensive, Kel. If he won't come down $5,000 on both, we won't buy them. I like the sound of everything else. Get to work on the pricing and go with your gut, Kel. I trust your judgment."

Her support meant the world. I buckled down and after some effort, I finally felt confident to make an offer on two-thirds of my original list. Of course Bard wouldn't be happy. But that wasn't the reason I was here.

The antique dealer's eager eyes narrowed when he came to the screens.

"Your mother wants them for $5,000 less? That's ridiculous. They're eighteenth century!"

"Yes, she's aware." Further explanation wasn't necessary; Francine knew her stuff. Bard snarled derisively and my stomach flipped.

The man stared at the list for a long time before pulling off his glasses and piercing me with his cold blue eyes.

"I must say I am disappointed in you, Kelly. Your list is woefully inadequate. I'm going to have to call your mother."

I managed an obsequious nod.

"Of course, Bard. I'll zip out and let you speak freely."

I choked down a coffee in a nearby cafe and dragged myself back to the Lantern Shop some 20 minutes later. Bard ran a peremptory hand through his thick silver hair.

"Your mother saw sense. She and I have reached an agreement, dear."

Francine's surprising capitulation hit me hard.

"I'll arrange for the shippers to pick the lot up first thing tomorrow." As he imperiously flicked the sales slips at me, I refused to let it end there.

"Thank you for everything, Bard. It was an honor to view your beautiful collection and I hope your health holds."

"Well, I hope you learned a thing or two. This business isn't for everyone."

I barely noticed the oppressive heat bouncing off the sidewalk as I stomped back, my anger directed mostly at Mom. She promised to stand firm. Why send me here if only to let Bard have his way? The whole thing could have been handled over the phone.

Once back at the hotel, I kicked off my shoes, sat on the bed and ran my eyes over the saleslips.

I couldn't believe it. Francine hadn't let me down at all. We were not only buying everything at the prices I suggested, but also the Japanese gold leaf screens, each for $5,000 less. Of course the wily Bard made me think otherwise; his fragile ego couldn't let the upstart proxy win.

CHAPTER 25

Francine Handles Customs

Wendy offered up an interesting proposition shortly after my return from Honolulu. She needed someone to accompany her three-year-old twin daughters Ashley and Chelsea to San Francisco for the weekend. If I agreed, we'd spend the weekend there with her and Peter before flying home together on Monday.

I loved the Bay Area and immediately agreed, only to be informed of a teensy hiccup.

All of the direct flights were full, so the girls and I would fly into San Jose. Peter would arrange for a car service to drive us up to San Francisco.

It would be my nieces' first flight and we prepped them for every eventuality. I was one smug auntie when the girls skipped into the airport's US Customs area, each clutching a beloved Cabbage Patch doll. The lineup was a little bit long, but the girls handled it well. When I finally handed over my passport to the balding officer in his mid-50s, I grinned at them as he rifled through the document.

"How long are you in San Jose?" he asked.

"An hour." As he reached for the entry stamp, I breezily added, "Their father has arranged a car service to zip us up to San Francisco."

His eyes hardened and whipped back and forth between the girls.

"Is he your husband?"

Ashley and Chelsea, normally very shy, suddenly giggled and shook their heads and I rushed to explain.

"No, he's my brother-in-law."

The gentleman dropped the stamp, splayed his large hands upon my open passport and skewered me with a cold stare. My mouth grew dry. I'd broken the golden rule of Customs' interrogations, that of never embellishing.

"Do you have written permission to take these children out of Canada, Ma'am?"

The clipped tone stabbed at my heart and the floor shifted. I had books, crayons, chocolate, Gravol, wet wipes, blankets, dolls ... everything but that.

"I have the parents' verbal permission, sir," I bleated pathetically.

"Well, that's concerning. How do I know that you're not absconding with them?" When I offered nothing but a blank stare, he snapped, "Report to Secondary Inspections and Services."

The next interviewer was equally taciturn. I tiptoed through the briefest explanation of the situation, highlighting my inability to contact their parents. This was years before cell phones and I hadn't a clue about the couple's Denver convention schedule. As the man stared at me in frank disbelief, Chelsea tugged on my sleeve.

"Are we on the plane now, Ahwee?"

The man's face shifted.

"Not yet, love." I smiled at her, and feeling slightly emboldened, attempted to further chip away at his official demeanor.

"The girls created the nickname 'Ahwee' when they were 18 months old and have been calling me that ever since."

The officer glanced back down at their earnest faces and sighed.

"Is there anybody who can confirm that you are allowed to take these girls into the United States, Ma'am?"

I could have hugged him.

"My mom! She'll give you the entire lowdown. I work with her. You can reach her at our Asian antiques store."

With just 45 minutes to make the flight, our hopes now rested solely with my boss. I hustled the girls to the bank of white plastic chairs as he dialed the number. There was a brief pause before he dismissively shook his head.

"The line's engaged."

Of course. Francine was up at The Granville Diner buying her tea.

"She'll be right back. We always leave the phone off the hook when we're out so folks don't think the shop's closed for the day. Please try again in a few minutes, sir," I pleaded. "She will pick up."

On his next attempt, she did. I leaned forward with all of the eagerness of a horse at the starting gate. We desperately needed the win.

"Ma'am, it's US Customs at Vancouver International Airport calling. I need you to answer some questions regarding the travel plans of Ms. Kelly Robinson. Yes, Ma'am, US Customs. I need to verify your relationship."

Francine soon had the officer reduced to monosyllabic splutters. He was clearly being treated to a minute-by-minute breakdown of our trip's itinerary; not even Fiona, our favorite travel agent, could have done better.

"Thank you, Mrs. Robinson, you've been most helpful." He hesitated and then smiled into the phone. "Yes, I do know South Granville and I will stop by your store on a day off, thank you. I look forward to it, also."

I began to gather up our belongings.

"However, there is just one more question before I let you go, Mrs. Robinson."

Just one? Excellent. We were as good as on that plane.

"What is your daughter's birthdate?"

I beamed at the girls. But then, after the slightest of pauses, the gentleman's demeanor suddenly shifted. The officer's eyes were once again scarily alert.

"No. That's the wrong date, Ma'am. Think carefully." There was another pause before the frown deepened and he repeated the question.

Seriously? Our imminent release was suddenly slipping away because my own mother couldn't answer the most basic of questions?

"Yes, Ma'am, I do understand that you're in your 60s and that it's been years since your youngest child was born but I'm sorry, no. I cannot just tell you." His eyes widened in astonishment. "And no. Asking Kelly is *not* an option."

Our flight would depart in less than half an hour. My heart ached as the girls hugged their dolls to their chests. They were now aware that something was amiss. Our keeper glanced down at the pair of soft blankets puddling woefully onto the ground and sighed.

"Enough. Thank you, Mrs. Robinson. Goodbye."

When the officer next spoke, it was in a voice tinged with wonderment.

"Your mother is quite something, isn't she?"

I slowly nodded.

"She was able to confirm everything about your trip, right down to tonight's potential room service order. Amazing." The tiniest smile flickered across his face. "But you seriously need to get her up to speed on your birthday." He banged his official stamp down onto my passport and briskly waved us through.

Francine filled in the blanks the following Tuesday. Her recall of my birthdate wasn't a total washout. She remembered the month and the year, just not the actual day. I gave her the biggest hug before quietly whispering it in her ear.

CHAPTER 26

Uncrating the Mothering Versus the Smothering

"Your Honolulu shipment has cleared Customs. Where do you want it delivered?"

Damn.

I ached to just hang up on the stranger. Doing so meant I wouldn't have to talk to the boss, which would be good. We weren't currently conversing.

Francine had seemed very positive about my decision to join the marathon training clinic at the local YMCA. But this morning, she dropped the facade.

"You look absolutely exhausted, Kelly. Go home and curl up on the couch for the day. I'll be fine here alone ..."

Instead of calmly reassuring her, I viciously lashed out like a nutter. The memory of her face crumpling in shock still haunts me.

What set me off? The lack of boundaries. At this point in my tenure, I expected Francine as my boss at work, not my mother. Today's innocent mothering felt like outright smothering. How could she not understand that the goal of successfully completing a marathon was a positive? It's not like I was doing it foolishly. The Y's Sunday marathon clinic was a quality outfit and yesterday's session was only four miles longer than my routine six-milers. I felt elated, not exhausted. God help me. What would the woman suggest when the mileage amped up into the upper teens? Total bedrest?

I might have overreacted just a tad.

You see, Francine wasn't privy to the whole picture. She had no clue that it wasn't just about running a marathon before I turned 30 in August. She didn't know that it was also about hopefully giving my personal life a serious reboot.

With both of my best friends no longer living in Vancouver, my social circle still consisted mostly of family members and a handful of customers, many of whom were at least twice my age. I needed to branch out and meet new, like-minded people. I loved running and thought the shared pain of a marathon would be great for bonding. It was a win–win.

I didn't dare tell Francine that I was desperate for more friends. She'd ache to help, something I avoided more than a root canal ever since she set me up five years ago with the son of a friend. He was a perfectly nice chap, however, the two of us were as different as warm milk and chilled chablis. The last thing I needed was a repeat performance with similar candidates. No, I was 29 and quite capable of acquiring my own friends, thank you very much.

Almost 40 years later, I realize that I was the delusional one. It took the writing of this book to finally peel back *all* the layers and unearth the real reason I signed on for that very first run clinic. It was because I needed to achieve something singular all by myself. My previous boss was my brother-in-law and my current one was my mother. Hello. Neither hired me solely based on merit. In order to successfully complete a marathon, however, it didn't matter who I was related to, only I could push myself to run the 26.2 miles. Successfully doing that would go a long way to silencing my self-doubts.

In the end, common sense won out. I apologized for my abhorrent behavior and handed Francine the phone. We couldn't take on storage charges because of a little spat. As she arranged for the seven crates to be delivered to Tolmie that afternoon, my evening plans slotted into place. It would be a long night.

Perhaps recognizing the need for a neutral buffer between us, Francine came up with a game changer of a plan.

"What if we recruited some of our regulars to help us tonight, Kel?"

I liked it. It would be a welcome and refreshing alternative to our usual triumvirate of Godfrey, Francine and me.

Three couples agreed to join us at Tolmie at 7 p.m.

Pierre, a dapper Quebecois, who'd made Vancouver his home for a decade, arrived first with his partner Brian. Only a year older than me, Pierre was reluctantly working as a Vancouver city bus driver. He hoped to eventually teach English in Japan. One of Francine's earliest customers, he was a true collector who sourced quality Japanese antiques from retailers throughout the Pacific Northwest. Brian, less of an aficionado, was a strapping fellow of over six feet and could easily play the lead in any Tom Selleck biopic.

Relative newcomers Evelyn and Noah arrived next. When Evelyn openly admired Francine's clanging oval jade bracelets on her first visit to the shop, we showed her FROG's versions. While not oval, they were blessed with the same soft green moss color. She plucked up the smallest one and shoved it onto her wrist. I grinned at her startled response to Francine's suggestion to "treat it to lunch." Unfortunately, the poor girl returned an hour later, most embarrassed. The bracelet refused to come off, despite her best efforts. We introduced her to our neighborhood jeweler. He sprayed her wrist with a few shots of Windex glass cleaner and the bracelet slipped away like fried eggs in a teflon pan. Evelyn had worn it daily ever since.

Amateur locksmith Susan and her partner Beth arrived soon afterward. We weren't surprised that they'd thoughtfully brought extra crowbars and hammers.

We got to it. Brian and Susan manned the crowbars, worrying them between the battered wooden boards with ease. Evelyn and Noah freed the tightly wrapped parcels and circulated them between Beth, Pierre, and me. We hurled the discarded paper at Godfrey who bunched it up into the tightest balls possible and tossed them into the empty crates. Francine appointed herself chief inspector, checking carefully for breakage and authenticity. The front hall was soon overflowing with bronze cranes, lamps and Buddhas, wooden tables, chairs, boxes and countless beaded tapestries and lacquered screens.

The difference between this and the previous uncrating sessions was staggering. Rather than the usual familial grumbling over smashed thumbs or crushed toes, tonight's atmosphere was convivial and enthusiastic. And quick. Once the seven semi-dissembled crates were hefted into the driveway just two hours later, Francine welcomed everyone upstairs for wine.

When my paternal grandparents passed away in the late '70s, Francine and Godfrey renovated the house and moved in. While Godfrey had an office downstairs, the main rooms were located on the second floor to take advantage of the spectacular view. The living room, with its huge windows overlooking the ocean and coastal mountains, was a combination of a mini art gallery and

FROG. The dove-gray walls were blanketed with colorful Canadian artwork and the majority of the furnishings were Asian antiques that had been thoughtfully acquired over two decades.

Tonight's guests appreciated Francine's unique decorating eye. They raved over her deliberate splitting of the tansu sections rather than the usual stacking, how she wasn't afraid to mix Canadiana items with 200-year-old Asian pieces and, most of all, how nothing was considered too precious or fragile. Everything had a practical function. The convivial conversation quickly moved on to questions about certain pieces in the newly unveiled shipment. With our blessing, the group soon split into individual couples and slipped downstairs for a closer look at coveted items.

Francine had hit on a novel idea. The invitees not only got first dibs on the contents, but they also felt special, singled out and seen. They understood that we weren't asking just anyone to help. We included only people we genuinely connected with and recognized as having a deep affinity for Asian antiques and collectibles.

As thanks for their tireless efforts, it was only right that they be offered Family Prices on everything. Each couple took home at least one treasure. Crate-opening night was now the ultimate presale.

The antiques world is very small. Word soon got out. Other regulars began asking if they could attend subsequent crate-opening parties. The tiresome slog of a job quickly evolved into a successful, fun FROG event and we opted for it more often than not.

CHAPTER 27

True Colors

I smiled at the toddler tucked snugly into Doris's hip as she and Francine encircled a pair of Korean wedding baskets. Life had changed greatly for Doris over the past two years. Now married to Ben, she was pregnant with their second child.

"Originally used for the bride's dowry items, the baskets are popular decorative pieces in Western homes," Francine explained. "The storage is deceiving. They may look small but you can hide a lot in them. I keep pens, pencils and writing paper in ours. I might buy another to store some towels by the bathtub." Francine paused to cheerfully waggle two fingers at the baby. He rewarded her with a toothless grin. "These are $700 each. Unfortunately, the margins are too low and I can't do your usual 15 percent discount. However, if you wanted both, you could have them for $1,200."

As Francine pried off a lid and removed the top tier, Doris shifted the lad onto her opposite hip and leaned in for a closer look.

"Oh, wouldn't they be just perfect under the ancestor portraits, Frankie? Can you put them aside for me? I'll try and get Ben to come in today for a peek." She sighed, running fingers through her curly hair. "I'd best get this little guy home for his nap."

When her husband dropped by later that afternoon, he made no effort to hide his annoyance that Francine wasn't there to greet him.

"Jackie's keeping banker's hours I see ..."

I rushed to disabuse him.

"*Frankie* left early to cook dinner, Ben. She's got a couple coming over to her house tonight to check out a Japanese mizuya."

Shut up, Kelly. FROG was Francine's shop. She was free to come and go as she pleased.

The narrowed eyes were the only clue that he'd heard.

"Show me those baskets Doris was going on about," Ben snarled.

We clambered onto the raised platform at the back and he immediately grabbed a price tag.

"Seven hundred dollars each? You've got to be kidding. They're just baskets." He slowly straightened up and folded his arms. "I'm not paying more than $900 for the pair."

This was a classic example of how he became a self-made gazillionaire. Ben refused to pay full price. Ever. I'd grown accustomed to watching Francine banter back and forth with him until they arrived at a mutually satisfactory price. I knew he'd expect the same today. However, the previous month's less than stellar financials had left me bruised and feeling that we needed to make more money on these baskets. But how? Ben smirked as I consulted the inventory book. The next few minutes could prove interesting.

"Okay, Ben, you can have them both for $1,200, which is a savings of more than ten percent."

The man's face was a medical wonder. It quickly transitioned from a mottled pink, then a most unflattering pasty white before finally settling into heart-attack gray.

I braced for his next move.

It was one I'd not seen before. His right foot slammed onto the carpet with a petulant stomp.

That sealed it. I was prepared to absorb the seven-percent taxes on the $1,200. But not now. He'd poked the bear.

I lowered my voice to just above a whisper and smiled.

"Naturally, you'd have to also pay the taxes."

Drops of spittle flew from his lips as he leaned forward to roar in my face.

"Absolutely not, Missy. I refuse to pay over $900 for the pair. Get Jackie on the phone. Now."

Not only did Ben still have my mother's name wrong, but also he was treating me and the baskets with utter disrespect. Just six months ago I would have buckled. But not now. These baskets were treasures and they deserved to live with someone who understood and respected them. Francine would feel the same.

"As you wish, Ben."

I did my best to ignore his triumphant snigger.

"Hi, *Frankie*." I paused, shooting Ben a side-eye before willing myself to speak calmly. "Ben's here about the baskets. I looked them up and the best we can do is $1,200. However, Ben won't go a nickel over $900. What do you think?" Another brief pause. "You're sure? Yes, Doris loves them. Okay. Thank you. Bye."

I smiled sweetly as I shared Francine's verdict.

"*Frankie* reluctantly agrees that you may have them both for $1,200, but only because Doris loves them so much."

The man's carotid veins pulsed and his hands balled into two tight fists. Without saying another word, he stormed out. Was I crushed? Not in the least. I'd lost a sale, but held onto my dignity.

When Doris returned the next morning brandishing a check for the full $1,200 – plus the tax – neither of us mentioned her husband. I also refrained from sharing that the phone's dial tone had subbed in nicely for Francine. Some things were best left unsaid.

CHAPTER 28

Business Up Front,
Party in the Back

"**D**ammit! Kelly, do we have any tweezers? I think it's gone right in."

I bent over Mom's proffered digit and could just make out a protruding chocolate-colored tip. The sliver was deeply embedded. Poor Francine. She'd snagged her thumb on the coarse, elongated beak of a 125-year-old wooden Korean wedding duck. Unfortunately, I didn't hold out much hope of finding a pair of tweezers. We were lucky if our shop's first aid kit contained a single Band-Aid.

"Can I help, ladies?"

The booming query scared the living bejesus out of us both. Roughly ten years older than me, the stranger was well over six feet tall and the picture of capability in his plaid shirt, faded jeans and steel-toed work boots.

"I sure hope so. My mom has a sliver deeply embedded in her thumb," I explained.

"Yikes, that's gotta hurt." He produced a large red-handled Swiss Army knife from a back pocket in his jeans. "Shall I play doctor?" He winked, waggling it in front of Francine's face. "I'm Ed."

"You're an angel. I'm Frankie and this is my daughter Kelly. Bless you. I'd love your help. Let's go somewhere more private though. I'm liable to kick you."

I grinned as they scurried into the back office.

"Let's stand next to the noren (Japanese fabric divider or curtain) where there's a breeze, Ed," Francine directed.

"Well, this is cozy. Not quite how I imagined my afternoon," the affable fellow replied in an obvious attempt to put her at ease.

"Me, neither," his charge giggled.

"Okay, if you'll just hold still, Frankie, I'll have it out in a jiffy."

With the patient tucked safely away, I relaxed and smiled warmly as two middle-aged women entered the store. I didn't know them. Smartly dressed in wool pants, vertiginous heels and matching black Burberry raincoats, they nodded cursorily at me and began arguing about the authenticity of the Chinese blue and white bride's jar in the window. The shorter gal had apparently been given one for Christmas, but as hers had a wooden top, it clearly wasn't one of ours. She turned toward me.

"Is the blue and white jar in your window an antique or a knockoff?"

Before I could answer, Francine interrupted with a shrill, "You won't hurt me?"

"No, I promise to be gentle."

Ed's reassurance was rewarded with a guttural moan.

"Seriously? I've hardly touched you, Frankie! You must hold still. It won't be good for either of us if you move. I won't be able to get a proper grip." Ed's baritone rocketed about the room.

"Good heavens, Shelagh, where are we?" the taller woman asked, her jaw gaping.

"I thought this was Frankie's. But maybe, we're ..."

Sensing understandable confusion, I rushed to clarify.

"Yes, you're at Frankie's. The blue and white jars ..."

Shelagh grabbed her friend's sleeve and pointed towards the office.

The sight of Mom's sneakers and Ed's boots, now snuggled toe-to-toe below the billowing office curtain, was truly riveting.

"I can't do anything if you keep pushing me away, Frankie!"

Someone gasped.

"Yes, so anyway, each jar is unique ..." I desperately tried to redirect.

"Quickly man. In and out!"

"Pinching in three-two-one. No. You moved, Frankie!"

"I'm sorry. It's the anticipation. You need to just do it quickly, Ed."

"Right. Quick in, quick out. It'll hurt less if you take a deep breath and then slowly let it out. Okay. On three. One ... two ... three."

"Ahhhhh, Ed! Stop! That hurts!" I could taste Francine's pain, her anguished groan was visceral. The fellow's voice morphed into that of a sympathetic father soothing his colicky infant.

"It always does, at first. I know, I know. Poor you. I can't get enough traction. I'm going to have to penetrate. I'm sorry, but it's the only way."

With the customers' faces now pinched in abject shock and disbelief, I capitulated. What jar? The disturbing dialogue behind the curtain was the sole attraction now.

"Stop! No more. Not without lubricant."

"We don't need lubrication, Frankie. I'm almost there. Just

one more pinch, and yes! Man, that's a big one!"

I whooped and turned toward the women, only to find they'd fled.

The dears never did learn the truth. The bride's jar wasn't a knockoff. It was the genuine article.

CHAPTER 29

Tapping into Hong Kong

Was I looking forward to my first overseas buying trip in the spring of '86? Not really. I was too focused on figuring out the running logistics. There would be just six weeks left until the marathon when we returned to Vancouver, so I needed to keep training while we were away.

Determined to keep me safe while running in Hong Kong and Bangkok, Francine purchased a high visibility vest and a rape alarm. I was upset about the vest. This was the mid-'80s, when only the running tights were colorful. It would be years before anyone other than airport tarmac employees would even consider donning something like Francine's shockingly orange, boxy number with its luminescent lime green stripes. I got that she wanted me to be visible but this was over the top. The rape alarm? Completely unnecessary. I'd been deafening folks with my shrill four-fingered whistling technique since the eighth grade. But I packed it to keep the peace.

It was still dark at 5:30 a.m. when I slipped the vest over my white sweatshirt and purple running pants on our first day in

Hong Kong. I was nearly at the elevators when Francine remembered the rape alarm.

Yesterday's ten-and-a-half-hour flight had taken its toll, leaving me sluggish and dreading the impending 9-mile run. However, the outside temperature was a refreshing 60 degrees and the air was laced with the aroma of freshly baked bread. I wasn't alone. Streams of smartly dressed men and women walked to work along the wide, well-lit boulevard.

My route was intentionally flat. I ran for 45 minutes before a thin sliver of dawn finally cracked through the inky darkness. It was time to head back. However, the pulsating lights of some emergency vehicles got me shooting off course.

Hong Kong's finest were still unspooling a huge roll of yellow police tape. As I crept closer, I could just make out the two uniformed officers squatting over the body of an adult male laying in a pool of viscous liquid. Francine's reflective vest unfortunately announced my presence. As the officers quickly draped a large sheet over the corpse, things got real. What was I doing running alone in a dark alley with my parched tongue plastered to my palate? So much for any potential finger-whistling. I gratefully palmed the rape alarm and bolted back to the hotel, shaving a good five minutes off my personal best time.

Francine's kindness, a hot shower and hearty breakfast worked wonders. I felt restored and excited to explore her favorite Hong Kong haunt. The antique store was renowned among serious collectors and dealers for its meticulously sourced pieces from China, India, Japan and Korea.

The elegant venture in the heart of Kowloon was already bustling with more customers than FROG saw in a week. I laughed when Francine caught me checking out the ragged, pea-sized hole in her left canvas running shoe.

"Don't laugh, Kel. If it's good enough for Mrs. Park, it's good enough for me."

We headed for the contemporary section where we immediately fell for the beautiful display of lacquered boxes in the shape of jumbo peanut shells and clamshells and life-size bunnies and ducks.

"Let's get twenty of each," Francine enthused.

I jotted them down in my notebook. But not the prices. I couldn't see any price tags. Francine wasn't worried.

"Would it be possible to view some of the older Chinese pieces?" She called out to a passing salesman.

He seamlessly handed us over to a colleague on the second floor.

The selection on offer up here was museum quality. Eighteenth- and nineteenth-century lacquered screens hovered next to black-wood altar tables, chairs and beds. Rows of shelves containing porcelain stools, vases and plates loomed over gleaming display cases of exquisite jade jewelry, peacock feather hair ornaments and lacquered mirrors. My mother floated about, not in the least concerned about the missing prices.

The assistant volunteered to draw up our wish list and I happily surrendered my notebook. He jotted down notes for the next 15 minutes before inexplicably introducing us to Randall, yet another handler. This gentleman perused our proffered list before subtly nodding.

"Please wait here while I notify Clarice."

An extremely elegant Chinese woman in her late thirties soon glided in as if on wheels and beckoned for us to join her by the window. In the harsher light, I could see she was actually closer to 50. While her makeup and chignon were impeccable, her fingernails were the star of the show. A lacquered lipstick red, they extended a good half-inch from the tips of her fingers.

"I understand you run an interest in Vancouver, Canada? We are honored by your visit," she murmured in a soothingly plummy voice.

Francine modestly dipped her head, unfortunately drawing attention to her shoe. The merchant's derisive lip-curl vanished so quickly I wondered if I'd imagined it.

"Thank you. Clarice is the manager, Kelly, " Francine explained. "I have visited your lovely establishment before, Clarice. I'm prepared to make a much larger purchase today, should we receive agreeable prices."

As Clarice ushered us to a nearby seating arrangement of four nineteenth-century blackwood chairs and a low table, Randall remained standing. He quickly flipped through the pages of my notebook and began speaking.

"First off, the contemporary lacquer items. Twenty each of the lacquered ducks, rabbits, peanuts and shells. Our retail price is 150 Hong Kong dollars each. You may have them for …"

Clarice suddenly stirred as he fell mute. She cupped her right hand and began tapping two talons in a staccato-like flourish upon the surface of a gleaming altar table. I discreetly checked for scratches.

"100 Hong Kong dollars each. Moving on to the antique wooden bowls. They retail for $350 Hong Kong dollars. You may have them for …"

Tap. Tap. Tap.

"$200 Hong Kong dollars each."

Francine's eager hunting dog stance reassured me. I wasn't losing it. The manager was communicating through her talons. Randall sailed on.

"Moving on to the cloisonné items…"

We were treated to this singular talon-tapping pricing system for the next hour. Once our list was exhausted Clarice glided out. Randall remained.

"I imagine you'll want to discuss your purchases in peace. May I get either of you a beverage as you do so? Water, Pepsi, Coke, or perhaps a gin and tonic?" he asked.

We opted for water. Now was definitely a time for clear heads.

CHAPTER 30

Always Check
the Wrapping

W e could have run into language barrier issues in Thailand as few dealers spoke English and we hadn't a lick of Thai. However, we managed just fine, thanks to our honorary Thai partner, Pook.

We have some bronze cranes to thank for our introduction to Pook. Francine bought a pair of contemporary 5-foot bronze cranes from a dealer in Honolulu, early on in my employment. When they sold within days, she ordered two more pairs. As Godfrey cracked open the wooden crate, a slip of paper floated to the floor. Francine snatched it up and was thrilled to discover the name and address of the shipper. She fired off a letter, asking for a potential crane source. Pook, the shipper's eldest son, responded quickly. He agreed to ship several more pairs to FROG and offered to be of further assistance should we ever visit his country.

We met him three years later. In his late 20s, Pook had a trust-worthy, open face with a thrusting underbite. During our many interactions, he was always professional and courteous. He took great care ensuring that we visited a variety of antique shops throughout Bangkok. We focused on unique items, such as antique beaded and sequined fabrics, wooden temple carvings, wooden and bronze table bases, lacquered boxes and ancient elephant bells. He personally wrapped the smaller pieces in sturdy brown paper and string, and ensured the rest were delivered to his business in a timely manner.

Pook quickly realized my key role was to help Francine determine whether we could sell something for a reasonable price and if so, how many we should purchase. When we started to argue, he'd leave us to sort it out. The road to acquisition was often bumpy, particularly with the uniquely flamboyant pieces. The more I dismissed something as a nonstarter, the more Madame Wasabi advocated for its potential.

Pook would quietly reassure the startled shopkeepers when I'd urgently hiss, "Do we really need all twelve, Francine? Would it not be better to buy just four? As you always say, 'less is more' and four would make them very special."

To her credit, Francine would usually give in.

"Kelly's our bookkeeper. She understands the financials much better than me. We'll have to settle for four."

And four it would be. The combination of Francine's flair for originality and my determination to not overspend made for some unique and worthy purchases. Pook ensured everything arrived safely in Vancouver.

We were delighted when he agreed to accompany us to Chiang Mai, northern Thailand's largest city. But even he couldn't keep me from making a critical error at a ceramic factory.

CHAPTER 31

Chiang Mai Takeout

We'd never have found the ceramic factory if not for Pook. The remote small family business was accessible only via a narrow unpaved road that wound randomly through the lush countryside. However, there was no mistaking it when we finally arrived. The property was strewn with hundreds of colorful pots ranging in size from tiny, elegant vases to corpulent vats.

Pook was immediately greeted as an old friend and whisked away, leaving us in the care of May, the owner's daughter. A recent graduate from a Midwestern American college, she sympathized with our intolerance to the oppressive humidity, and immediately offered us chilled club sodas. I was grateful. Locals had warned us off the tap water, and the sketchy, rusty-capped bottles of tepid cola were growing very tiresome.

Once properly hydrated, Francine and I fanned out over the property and were pleasantly surprised by the vast variety of glazes. We were particularly taken with the wondrous blood-red *sang de boeuf* pots slashed with vivid streaks of turquoise or purple. They'd be entirely new to Vancouver and we suspected they'd move quickly.

When our large order was firmed up and settled, May twinkled like a child with a secret.

"As a token of his deep appreciation for your business, my father invites both of you to choose a souvenir. We'll include them in your shipment, so don't worry about the size."

This was a first. However, May wasn't finished. "We're also hoping that you could join us for lunch. My brother is going into Chiang Mai for takeout."

How kind. We eagerly accepted both offers, mindful of not being too greedy. Francine eventually settled on a lovely celadon green, eight-inch diameter pot while I opted for the equivalent in a beautiful cobalt blue. Stuffed with a small jade or ficus plant, it would be a lovely souvenir of this trip.

Francine and I playfully awaited brother's return by considering the potential options for lunch. Our best guess was either a luscious Pad Thai stir fry or one of the hearty, gingery chicken dishes with their spicy bowlfuls of rice. We'd be delighted with either. When the distinctive "putt-putt-putt" sounds of his small motorbike finally tootled up the long gravel driveway, Pook and 20 others magically appeared. They formed a raggedy horseshoe-shaped knot behind the long table erected in the outdoor courtyard. We weren't the only hungry ones.

I was surprised to spot just one tiny white plastic bag swinging from the chap's handlebars. When May's brother cheerfully produced two hamburger-sized Styrofoam boxes, my jaw tightened in panic. Pook's observant nod confirmed my suspicions. He and the others had already eaten. They'd gathered to watch the Canadians eat.

While I ached to crawl into the depths of some gigantic pot

for the rest of the visit, my mother relished the singular attention. I stared in astonishment as she enthusiastically pantomimed extreme hunger by circling a jazz hand over her tummy. The collective anticipation grew palpable as the esteemed guest raised the hinged lid and peeked inside.

Francine's deep revulsion was so fleeting I doubt anyone noticed. She masterfully slapped on a chillingly vacant smile reminiscent of a Barbie doll. When I whipped up my lid, I immediately understood why. A flaccid fried egg was perched on top of a curiously bulging white kaiser bun. Francine didn't do fried eggs hot, let alone stone cold. She needed help and fast. I began to prattle.

"Oh my. Goodness. I'm thirsty. Is it possible for us to have several bottles of club soda, May?"

Three two-liter plastic bottles magically appeared.

Excellent. Confident about Mom's ability to choke down the egg with mouthfuls of soda, I surreptitiously peeled back the top half of the bun and immediately gagged. I'd never seen anything like the mysterious chunk of meat. The color could best be described as a cross between a fiery blood-red and a deep inky-blue. Sensing my discomfort, Francine ventured a quick peek, and began to flap her hands so impulsively I grew concerned she'd take flight.

She then thumped her stomach with a tight fist. Upon regaining her speech, my mother's strangled voice was a good octave higher than usual.

"What a lovely treat! I am so very sorry that I won't be able to eat it! Bad tummy, bad tummy."

The crowd's understandable confusion inspired my mother to utter the unforgivable.

"Kelly will enjoy mine."

My throat closed. The concept of consuming one was challenging, two was inconceivable. However, this congealed egg and mystery meat concoction was obviously revered as a special treat for special guests. If ever there was a time for me to take one for the team, this was it. I braced and sunk my incisors into the gelatinous egg, through the powdery bun and then into the azure-tinged flesh.

While the taste was pleasantly reminiscent of roast chicken, I was challenged by the meat's texture. My teeth skittered over the rubbery surface, desperate for purchase. As the resilient lump lumbered on my tongue like a moribund slug, I snatched up the glass, swilled two mouthfuls of club soda and swallowed.

"How delishush," I squeaked before guzzling the rest of the glass.

Sweat beads now blossomed freely on my forehead as the sizable nugget slowly squeezed its way down my esophagus and I bit back impending nausea. Thankfully, the novelty of watching a Canadian eat quickly faded. As the folks began to drift off in clumps of twos and threes, Francine cheerfully waved her goodbyes and something inside me snapped.

"Thanks for nothing, Mother. This is godawful," I evilly hissed, incensed that the woman didn't appreciate my supreme sacrifice.

"Are you feeling any better, Frankie?" May's solicitous voice hovered suspiciously close and dread washed over me. Had this kind soul overheard? I dearly hoped not. The entire meal actually wasn't that bad. Those harsh words were solely meant for my mother's ears.

I couldn't resist stealing glances at May over the remaining half-hour. Was I imagining it, or was she talking mostly to Francine now? It was difficult to tell, her manners were impeccable. Mind you, when it came time to say goodbye, May hugged only my mother. But surely that was understandable. Our senior team member was ill. Or was it more than that?

I worried throughout the entire ride back to our hotel, but I suffered silently, knowing Pook would be horrified by my rude behavior. However, when I finally shared my concerns in the privacy of our room, Francine wasn't fussed.

"Vancouver is going to go crazy over the pieces, Kel, especially the sang de boeuf pots. I've never seen the likes of them anywhere. Let's just hope that everything arrives in one piece. But I think we can trust Pook to pack it properly, don't you?" When I didn't rush to reassure her, she took a closer look at me. "Are you feeling okay after that meal? Thank you so much for taking it on. I just couldn't face it."

"I'm worried about May, Mom. I think she overheard my derogatory comment regarding lunch."

"Oh, Kel, love, stop worrying. May probably didn't hear a thing, and if she did, I'm sure she's forgotten all about it. Now, let's go eat. I'm starving, aren't you?"

Food was the last thing on my mind.

Our Thai ceramic shipment arrived safely in Vancouver some six weeks later. The singular omission of the cobalt blue souvenir, my choice, spoke volumes. Lesson learned. I'd be very, very careful with my caustic remarks to Francine in public from now on.

CHAPTER 32

Bathing Suit Alternatives

Francine and I were looking forward to the three-hour air-conditioned coach tour to the Chiang Mai orchid farm. It would do us good to escape the sun for a bit. We weren't alone. A plump and balding fellow with one of the worst sunburns I'd seen in a long time was also patiently waiting at the hotel pickup point. One look and Francine whipped out the economy-sized sunscreen bottle from her bag.

"The sun is deceptively brutal here. Please, slather this on. All over."

I smirked as he gingerly dabbed minuscule dots of the thick sunscreen onto his fiery forehead. There was no way Mom would allow him to get away with that. Sure enough, his skin was soon glistening. He needn't reapply any more for the duration of the tour.

Once aboard, I leaned into the window as they got acquainted across the aisle. It would be nice to just sit quietly for a spell. My mother's boundless energy was exhausting at times. This trip had reaffirmed the notion of our different recharging methods. As an ambivert, I sometimes needed time alone while Francine, an extrovert, always benefitted from engaging with people. Overhearing that he was "Ole from Oslo" and on his first trip to Thailand, I knew I was golden. Francine loved Norway.

"You come from a lovely part of the world, Ole!" As he expressed delighted surprise, Francine nodded. "This is also our first time visiting Thailand. We're actually on a buying trip for our Vancouver antique store but we're taking the afternoon off," she giggled naughtily.

"Thailand's very different than I expected, I have to say." Ole's voice faded as he rubbed his slick, lotioned hands through his thinning hair. "It's been quite difficult traveling alone."

Francine kicked into Mamasan Frankie mode.

"Well, Ole, you're more than welcome to hang out with us today. Do you have dinner plans?"

We were now a party of three.

The orchid farm was a horticultural wonder. Draped with shade nets and spread over several acres, it boasted a wide variety of orchids in every imaginable size, shape and color. Ole, an ardent gardener, was a new man upon our return to the hotel.

"Shall we meet up at the pool for a swim before dinner?" he asked, eyes brimming with hope.

"Absolutely. We'll join you in a jiffy," my mother confirmed.

Ten minutes later, Francine knocked on the bathroom door.

"I've left my bathing suit behind in Bangkok. Did you bring two, Kel?"

No. However, she was a good four inches taller than me and some 50 pounds heavier. Even if I had brought another one, it probably wouldn't fit.

"Ah well, I'll make do with whatever I can find in the gift shop. You go on ahead, I'll join you soon," she called out cheerfully.

When I skulked onto the blisteringly hot deck clutching our two bath towels, an English newspaper and my novel, I was startled by the transformation of the normally morgue-like area. It was now all "Ipanema Beach at the height of summer." Dozens of deeply tanned, svelte bodies packed the deck. Most of the men flaunted classic black Speedos while the women sported dental floss thongs with either skimpy bikini tops or nothing but their gold chain necklaces.

Instantly chaste in my black one-piece, I was desperate for refuge. Of course Ole had nabbed three loungers in the remotest corner of the deck. It was all I could do to creep over. The sunburned Norwegian was oblivious to both the fashionistas and my extreme discomfort. As I hissed my intention to plunge in the pool, he shouted, "You go for a swim, dear. I'll watch for Mother." Excellent. Everyone now clocked the pale postulant as the daughter of Mr. Beetroot.

When Francine finally graced the pool deck, I was stunned speechless. The "make do" gift shop swimming costume was extraordinary. Even for my mother. Her much-loved white, industrial underwire bra, with straps so wide one could almost imagine them as landing strips for float planes, was bad enough. But she'd inexplicably paired it with an immense pair of men's bathing trunks. An unfortunate beige, they would have been a bit loose on Luciano Pavarotti. Perhaps going for a one-piece look, and a better fit, my mother had yanked them up and tucked them into the underwire. I held my breath as she dug into her leather bag for something else. A collective gasp gripped the deck as she slowly unfurled the plastic, see-through shower cap sourced upstairs in our bathroom. Oblivious to her impact on the other hotel guests, she plunked it on her head, puffed it out and carefully tucked in any wayward strands, effectively completing her transformation to that of the Pillsbury Doughboy. I plunged back into the water as she strode toward us.

Ole took it one further. He simply vanished. We never set eyes on the Norwegian again.

CHAPTER 33

A Robinson Trifecta

I was thrilled to discover our Bangkok hotel was directly across from an ideal location for my training runs: the 142-acre Lumpini Park.

Francine was excited, too.

"I'll hang out in the park when you run, Kel. You can leave the rape alarm and vest behind."

Excellent.

It was still dark when we arrived at the entrance. The park was popular with other runners; I could hear their footfalls on the pavement as I began the nine-miler. However, the humidity was surprisingly intense. It was like running in a sauna. I soon felt quite miserable and it wasn't until the sun came up that I noticed the monks. Dozens of saffron-robed Buddhist monks were lined up along the groomed path, silently accepting alms from countless devotees.

Francine sang out as I trundled past on my third loop.

"Check out the monks' feet, Kel!"

While many were wearing some form of an open-toed sandal,

several simply went barefoot. It was most humbling. Who was I to dread running the remaining paltry six miles in a pair of comfy sneakers?

Pook met us at the hotel a few hours later. We spent the morning prowling through several small shops in an antiques area of Bangkok. The variety of treasure on offer was outstanding. We focused on the exotic – gilt-laden Buddhas, quilted beaded blankets and deeply carved wooden elephant wall plaques.

By the time Francine and I returned to the hotel for a late lunch, we were hangry; never optimal for our relationship. I gave her lots of space as she steamed toward the back of the air conditioned restaurant.

As Francine's leather tote suddenly slipped off her shoulder and slammed into a fresh pint of beer on a nearby table, I slipped into the nearest booth. I watched spellbound as the glass skittered off and soared into the elderly gentleman's lap. Mom sprang into action, snatching up cloth napkins as if she was about to stanch a life-threatening bleed. The poor fellow froze in anticipation of her next move. Thankfully, a server swooped in with thick towels and a replacement pint before Francine could make actual contact.

My mother hovered anxiously as the patron spread the towels over his soggy lap.

"I am SO very sorry, sir. Do let me pay for your lunch."

He bowed his head, avoiding eye contact.

"That's very kind, Madame. Thank you. However, there's no need."

My heart went out to this innocent; he'd no idea who he was dealing with.

"But you're soaked! Please let me take care of your dry cleaning!"

He shifted uncomfortably in his chair.

"That isn't necessary, but thank you."

"Well, then, at least allow me to pay for the beers, please," she beseeched.

The gentleman sighed and locked eyes with the server, who nodded and gently grasped Francine's elbow.

"Thank you, Madame. Please understand that there is truly no need for you to do anything. The gentleman dines here regularly."

"All the more reason for me to pay!" Francine exclaimed.

After guiding her to my table, the server leaned in and whispered, "It's okay, Madame. Honestly. He owns the hotel. He'll just slip up to his suite to change." She smiled reassuringly. "Now, please relax and enjoy your lunch."

I looked over at Mom and giggled.

"You took out the hotel *owner's* beer?"

"Oh, Kel. I feel dreadful."

I simply laughed, yet again.

Silly me. I knew better than to tempt karma.

"Here they are, Kel."

Francine waved as the shiny Toyota sedan pulled up to the hotel curb at noon the next day. I felt a bit nervous as I'd never met these friends of my parents before. My mother beamed as the hotel bellhop, dressed in a gold brocade cropped jacket and matching pair of voluminous pantaloons, bowed and pulled open the back door. I slid in on the other side and settled my purse on the floor.

It was as if we'd stepped into a high-end spa. The air-conditioned vehicle was immaculate, with soft tunes tinkling from hidden speakers. The couple, both in their early 40s, exuded tranquility. Anong was beautiful. Her long, shiny black hair shimmered like a curtain down the back of her cotton shift. Her husband, Pilat, looked very kind. Tidy and trim, he turned around to smile shyly at me as Francine launched into introductions.

"Kel, this is Dad's great friend, Pilat. He's one of Thailand's top pediatricians. His wife, Anong, is a nurse ..."

A deafening shriek suddenly ripped through the car.

The couple clamped their hands firmly over their ears, spluttering, "What is that dreadful noise?"

Francine assumed control by fanning her door and hollering, "Thai killer bees! Thai killer bees!"

The startled bellhop reacted by zooming around the car, wildly flapping his arms in time with her efforts. We'd landed in a horror film.

I dared not move for fear of being stung. However, as the crippling, all-consuming screech raged on, I became aware of something odd happening down by my feet. My purse was thrashing about on the floor as if possessed. The murderous swarm must be trapped inside. But that was impossible. The opening was tightly zipped.

I suddenly remembered the rape alarm. I'd chucked it in my purse when Francine offered to come to the park. Was it the caterwauling offender?

A cursory peek confirmed it. The little devil was working overtime. I snatched it out and rolled it in my hand, desperately searching for an off button or the battery casing cover. But the alarm's plastic surface was as smooth as a baby coconut.

I threw open my door and hurled the alarm. It soared over the manicured lawns onto the road where it bounced once, then twice, before being crushed into sublime powder by a passing car. As a glorious silence descended, apologies and explanations spewed out of me in a babbling torrent.

"I'm so very sorry. It's not killer bees. It's my rape alarm. My rape alarm somehow self-activated! I'm so sorry."

I flinched as our innocent hosts slowly unglued their hands

from their ears and turned to stare at me in open astonishment. I couldn't blame them. Only a nutter brings a rape alarm to a pleasant lunch.

Unfortunately, the Robinsons weren't quite finished favoring Bangkok's finest hotel with our quirky behavior.

Francine has suffered from a mysterious esophageal pain for as long as I can remember. The affliction, which she calls "midline pain," attacks without warning and is utterly debilitating. As it mercifully disappears after just a few sips of cold milk, Godfrey suggested she always carry a thermos of milk on this trip, just in case.

On our fourth day in Bangkok, we hopped into a cab to spare Pook from the city's infamous early afternoon rush hour traffic. Our hotel was now within view, however all four lanes were choked with vehicles. It was one giant parking lot. We'd not moved for 15 minutes when Francine suddenly squeaked in alarm.

"I've got a midline pain bubbling up, Kel," she exclaimed, tapping her palm just below her collarbone.

"Help is but a sip away, Mom," I purred as she dove for her thermos.

She wrenched open the lid and we were slammed with a revoltingly sour odor. The neglected milk was undrinkable.

God only knew how long the pain would linger or if it would worsen. She needed help. Now! Our hotel's restaurant buffet had lots of milk. But there was no way my poor mother could tackle those four choked lanes of traffic; the pain always zapped her energy and left her flat.

"It's okay, Mom. You sit tight. I'll be right back with milk."

I bolted from the car and darted between the rows of idling vehicles, over the broad expanse of manicured lawn and up the hotel's endless driveway. I peeled off to the restaurant, blundered past the astonished hostess and straight through the lineup of folks patiently waiting their turn in the buffet line.

"I must get at the milk," I bellowed.

I grabbed a glass, lunged for the ladle resting in a large bath of milk and began wildly flinging. More milk flew out than in. I'd have to dip the glass into the bowl. Was one glass enough? No, I'd probably spill most of it scrambling back through the traffic. As I snatched up a second glass, a faint voice called out my name.

It was my dear mother. She slid into a chair and stretched out a limp arm. Everyone gasped as they realized this was a dairy emergency. Once the glass was drained and the patient slowly broke into a milky smile, the crowd applauded. She was going to be alright.

This scary episode left me shaken. But my mother was loquacious with relief and eager to explain her magical appearance.

"The driver thought you'd done a runner, Kel. But when I couldn't speak, he thought I was having a heart attack. He cranked the wheel, zoomed over the cement median, did a sharp u-turn and delivered me here. I hope he was happy with the tip …"

I couldn't say. I just knew that between the spilled beer, the screaming rape alarm and the hijacked buffet episodes, there wasn't enough money in the world to tip the hotel staff properly.

CHAPTER 34

A Close Call

Julia James was intrigued by the sound of the Thai ceramic pots.

"I could do with some unusual colors out on our patio. Please let me know the minute they arrive," she said, looking brightly about the shop. "Do you have any figurines in stock? Our living room could do with some character. I'm looking for something I can carry home because I walked down today. Any opportunity I get to be outside is a treat."

I shot a discreet look at the flight attendant's shoes. Always enviably quirky, today's pair didn't disappoint. The red and yellow buttery leather, lace-up flats were ideal for her steep walk home.

She made up her mind quickly, opting for Mrs. Sheldon's nineteenth-century Chinese incense burner in the shape of a Fu dog. Julia had chosen well; the male guardian lion's right paw was leaning on a ball, symbolizing protection.

As Francine began writing up Julia's bill, Mrs. Sheldon's son walked in. We hadn't seen him for four months and his physical transformation was alarming. Always on the lean side, his clothes now hung off him like a Chinese Shar-Pei's skin folds.

"Don't look so upset, Kelly. It's just my dicky heart, nothing to worry about. It's enlarged but I'll be fine as long as I stay on the meds. I'll gain the weight back, " he informed me dismissively. "The doc just gave me the green light to fly back to Bangkok. I leave tomorrow." Robert smiled eagerly and rubbed his hands together. "So, how much do you owe me?"

I nudged him into the office. We couldn't risk Robert discovering Julia's purchase. She was very private and wouldn't appreciate his questionable enthusiasm. It was a smart move. Robert was thrilled to learn he'd be getting a sizable check from us today. I didn't bother to mention that the majority of the pieces had found good homes. He wouldn't care. When I asked how his treasures were selling at the other stores, he chuckled and slapped his bony thigh.

"I have no financial worries whatsoever in Bangkok. I'm great."

I silently disagreed. Health is wealth. He might have the money to enjoy a carefree life in Bangkok, but that meant nothing if he wasn't well. The "dicky heart" was indeed troubling. However, he clearly preferred to focus on the monetary.

"Could you give me a breakdown of each piece, please, Kelly? I'd like an idea of what's popular and what to give you next time."

Once we'd exhausted the itemization, Julia and her incense burner were long gone. Francine pressed him regarding his medical diagnosis. He refused to discuss it.

"I'll see ya when I see ya," Robert cackled as he loped out.

The man was a veritable phoenix. He looked remarkably well when he popped in three months later. He'd regained all of the weight back and more. I never could have guessed the reason behind the transformation though.

"I'm hitched!" he squealed, raking bony fingers through his wispy bangs.

Pardon?

"You knew I met the wife on my very first day in Bangkok, right? I didn't tell you? Well, I'd just walked out of Customs when this lovely young Thai woman rushed up to me and introduced herself. She knew I was special."

My internal alarm bells were now jangling so loudly, I was surprised Robert couldn't hear them. There was something off about this whole scenario.

"Juliette was meeting her brother. His plane was late and I immediately asked her out on a date. She soon introduced me to the rest of her family. They adored me, especially when I made an honest woman of Juliette."

Who would marry this self-centered bloke? He had only one topic. Himself. There had to be more to it. Then again, I couldn't overlook that 180-degree health turn. Juliette had worked miracles on that front.

"Of course, I won't be returning to Vancouver as often. Juliette wants me home. Dorothy, my aunt, will pick up my checks."

Robert skipped out without sharing more.

Francine and I finally met the mysterious woman six months later. Aunt Dorothy couldn't be more different from her nephew. Tastefully dressed in a pale lavender cashmere twinset that nicely set off the silver highlights of her untouched hair, she apologized for not coming in sooner for Robert's money.

"It won't hurt my nephew to wait a couple of months." Acknowledging our startled looks, she shrugged. "My late sister foolishly believed he would keep her collection together. She'd be devastated if she knew the truth."

Francine carefully suggested, "Perhaps his marriage will make a new man of him."

The woman smiled sadly and shook her head. "No. It simply makes him a bigamist."

Like her nephew, Dorothy slipped out before we could learn more.

CHAPTER 35

Ins and Outs

Ever since Ed yanked the sliver from Francine's thumb, he'd quickly become a favorite FROG regular. We felt we'd gotten to know him quite well. He embraced the NNHE payment plan with gusto, purchasing mostly rustic clothing chests or *isho-dansu*. I enjoyed delivering them to his cozy home, where he was often in the kitchen whipping up a gourmet meal for his pair of beloved Shih Tzus.

It was quite disturbing to see him shuffle into FROG on a drizzly November morning. His greeting was oddly wooden. Francine flashed me a look of alarm as he suddenly held up his hands as if bracing himself.

"I have to share something with you both that I feel is long overdue."

Oh God. The man had cancer.

"I've come to treasure our friendship and I dearly hope my revelation won't alter that," he spewed, his voice cracking.

A revelation? Okay, not cancer. Something that would change our opinion of him. Perhaps jail time?

"The puppies and I live with my partner Waylon. I'm gay." As he clamped a handkerchief over his crumpled mouth, my throat closed. I couldn't trust myself to speak. Francine rallied admirably.

"Oh, Ed, I do thank you for sharing that." The warmth in her voice sparked some hope in his eyes. "I consider it an honor to be told. Please know that you're an absolute dear in my books. I'm sure Kelly feels the same."

I could only nod as the lump in my throat gave way to tears.

How very courageous. The man had no idea of our reaction, yet he chose to tell us. Of course, this confession wouldn't affect our opinion of him. He was still the same quality guy with the cheeky personality. I ached at the thought of him ulcerating over the revelation. How much sleep had it cost him? I staggered over and patted him awkwardly.

"I can now count on two hands the straight people who know," he confessed with a wobbly smile.

What a sobering tidbit. Ed was edging close to 40.

Francine paused a beat, before proceeding in a barely audible whisper.

"Forgive me if this is too intrusive, Ed, but I *must* ask. You are taking all ... appropriate precautions, I trust?"

God, Mom, seriously? I wanted to melt into the floor.

However, it had been only a year since Rock Hudson passed away from complications of AIDS, so of course her thoughts went there.

"Well, that was the one response I certainly did *not* anticipate. Thank you, Frankie," the astonished Ed grinned before adding, "Waylon and I have been together for over a decade."

Wow.

However, Ed wasn't finished.

"No one knows at work. No one. I'm running for the presidency

of our union and when you toss in the whole AIDS thing, well ..."
His voice faded away.

Over 35 years later, I'm staggered by how naive I was back
in 1986. We had many openly gay customers. The vast majority of them were in long-term, committed relationships. It never
occurred to me to consider how or when they came out. They
already were and I left it at that.

Ed's agony was an absolute shocker. I had a lot to learn. It was
like the shutters being flung open. What a staggering weight to
carry around, having to be so very careful to not slip up at work.
Ever.

Of course we'd honor his confidence. It wasn't our secret to tell.

Ed shifted in his chair and smiled sheepishly.

"There's more."

This poor man.

"I need a date for our Christmas party at work."

Francine nodded slowly and they both looked at me. I was
confused. Of course he couldn't ask Waylon. But why me? Why
not Francine? The penny dropped as the pair impishly smirked.

My thoughts bounced back and forth between "I'm an idiot" and
"He couldn't have picked anyone better." On the one hand, it was
madness. I barely knew the chap. Folks would recognize right away
that we weren't a couple. But then again, maybe it wasn't that silly.
I had a theater degree. How hard would it be to act for four or five
hours? Surely I could do this. Maybe. But then again, maybe not ...

When Ed arrived to pick me up, I barely recognized him. He
was dressed in a smart, well-fitting suit that was the antithesis
of the usual jeans, plaid shirt and steel-toed work boots. It was
comforting to discover that Ed was equally as nervous. His trem-
bling hands betrayed him. The red rose wrist corsage shook within
its clear plastic box.

"You needn't wear it, if you don't want to, Kelly," he rushed to reassure me.

That vulnerability melted my heart. I'd probably be the only gal sporting such a floral tribute, but so what. I clamped it on my wrist, vowing to give my best possible performance going forward.

The dinner dance was held in a festively decorated conference room of a swanky downtown hotel. There were already over a hundred people in attendance. Ed quickly sourced out the wine and then introduced me to the eight others at our table. The male colleagues quickly fell into hockey speak while their wives honed in on me.

"So, tell us, how did you and Ed meet?" the tone Milly politely chirped.

My date peeled away from the manly chit-chat regarding the mid-season form of the Vancouver Canucks and stick-handled a seamless reply.

"Oh, we've known each other for ages. Kelly and her mother run Frankie Robinson Oriental Gallery, the wonderful Asian antiques store. Surely you've heard of it?"

As Francine would say, that response certainly "put the cat amongst the pigeons." With the four gals now focused on the store, Ed winked at me and rejoined the sports chat. When the ladies moved onto the concept of buying overseas, I knew we were golden. Things continued to improve as the food arrived and the speeches began.

But then the after-dinner, pre-dance lull hit.

"We always do something special around Valentine's Day, don't we, girls?" Elaine twittered, gesturing to her husband to top up her glass. "Ed! You must bring Kelly to the February do!"

Ed kicked me under the table. We were officially a couple.

He confirmed the invitation early in the new year.

"Everyone's hounding me to bring you to the Valentine's do, Kelly. It'll be *very* different from the Christmas party," Ed teased. "Can you say, 'Monster Jam Demolition Derby?'"

I could. But ...

"Just picture huge trucks smashing into each other. You'll be deaf within the hour."

That last bit sold me. It meant little chance for random chit-chat.

The gang was already ensconced when Ed led the way to our seats, mere rows up from the dirt-filled pit. Bev, Milly, Elaine, Debbie and their husbands waved a friendly greeting. Ed shoved a pair of noise canceling earmuffs at me and warned, "Whatever you do, don't take them off."

It was wise advice. The pump 'em up music surged and I could just make out the introductory, "Rev your engines!" The crowd of thousands roared and leapt to their feet as six jumbo trucks equipped with impossibly enormous rubber tires bounced out into the pit. Now charging over the huge mounds of dirt at great speed, they smashed directly into each other, sending some rolling over the tops of others. It was pure carnival bumper cars come to life. When a victor eventually emerged, the losers either drove away or were towed off, and we were treated to several chest-thumping victory laps by the battered winner.

I suddenly flashed back to the symphony experience with Allan. This could not be more different.

"*Ladies and gents, are you ready for more?*" the announcer bellowed.

The crowd roared.

When the lights finally came up some two hours later, everything felt suddenly joyless. The area was strewn with crushed popcorn, tossed hotdog wrappers and empty plastic beer cups. I felt spent. My trigger? The sad reality that Ed's partner Waylon was forced to miss out. He should have been here.

Would there be a third date? I didn't think so.

CHAPTER 36

Moving On

It was as if I'd clicked my heels in triplicate, and boom, FROG needed a new home. By the end of 1986, we'd outgrown the 600-square-foot shop, thanks to the two huge consignment acquisitions and our overseas purchases. Francine and I were more than done with the requisite sidewalk showings and Tolmie Street viewings.

Our sights were set on "Antiques Row," the four-block strip on Granville Street, just around the corner. It was home to many antique and collectible shops. However, our timing was poor. Vacancies in late '86 were rarer than authentic Tang Dynasty camels. It would be several weeks before Francine would finally get a break.

The candidate was as narrow as our current 10th Avenue site, but twice as deep. The modern building was blessed with ample parking, lots of storage space, a decent heating system and an elevator. While the latter would certainly ease deliveries, and the indoor parking lot meant shelter from the rain, the top selling feature for me was the bathroom. It was utterly devoid of fungi.

Francine had one sticking point. The $25,000 key money payment. This practice of paying the current tenants as a thank you for enabling us to take over their lease was common practice during the tight '80s market in Vancouver, and independent of anything to do with the landlord. The hefty amount would be a challenge for FROG. Peter listened thoughtfully when Francine wisely presented her case over a hearty breakfast at Tolmie Street. We were relieved when he assured her the benefits would indeed outweigh the expense. Bucked by such strong support, my boss confidently forked over the key money and signed the lease. FROG was on the move.

Unlike the now infamous ceiling flood day of four years earlier, we engaged the professional help of Zac'll Move Ya. The moving company was a giant in my books. I've no idea how Francine first discovered the outfit and the origins of the name remain a mystery. The company was run by Al and his full-time employee, the gentle, blind-in-one-eye Bert. Random part-timers were drawn from a limitless pool of strong, young men.

Several curious neighbors stopped by on moving day to ask what we'd be selling. We quickly slapped large sheets of brown paper onto the windows. It had a curious effect. The inquisitive now dropped onto their knees and crooned through the letterbox, "Hellooooo! Can I come in? Just for a sec?"

Sorry, no.

The exhausted Francine and I were ripe for fractious mother/daughter meltdowns. Neither of us possessed one-tenth of the patience required for polite nattering with oblivious looky-loos.

The joint quickly morphed into construction central. The plethora of electricians, carpenters and painters worked feverishly to transform the elegant former jewelry store with its pink walls, multiple glass cabinetry and intimate nooks, into a smart antiques and collectibles showroom.

Once the spotlights and track lighting were finally sorted, the walls painted and the rear wooden platform built and carpeted, it was time to prep the inventory for our grand opening party on the evening of February 20th, some three short weeks away. I set up a furniture refinishing area in the quiet hallway next to the elevator, and leaned into the tricks I'd gleaned from a generous wholesaler in Hong Kong. He'd taught me how to burnish natural wood with simple floor paste wax, smooth out any rough edges with fine sandpaper, buff out nicks with black or brown shoe polish, and erase chips in lacquer surfaces with similar colored felt pens. Meanwhile, the boss attacked the office. She efficiently organized the bookshelves, reclaimed the desk and mapped out the storage area.

Once those tasks were dispatched, we did our best to heft, shove and nudge the inventory into optimum positions in the showroom. However, the place still resembled a hoarder's paradise with just two days remaining. We reached out to Ed and Pierre for help, knowing we could count on them to work diligently without much instruction. Both gents also possessed the requisite positivity.

I couldn't help comparing Ed's reality with that of Pierre, our French Canadian customer and frequent crate opener. He lived openly with his partner Brian (the Tom Selleck doppelganger) in a small, exquisitely decorated apartment in Vancouver's West End. Charismatic and impossibly handsome, Pierre was a fastidious dresser who was as fond of his looks as Bard was of his, but he tempered the effect with a wonderful sense of humor.

Over the past few months, Pierre was taking more and more time away from his work as a Vancouver city bus driver, due to stress or injury. He'd been dropping hints lately about switching jobs. However, we were gobsmacked by today's announcement.

"I've resigned."

"Oh, Pierre. Why?" Francine's concern echoed my own.

"I've been hired to teach English in Sendai! I'm moving to Japan in six weeks."

"Get out!" I screamed, stunned. He always said he would, but I never thought he'd act on it.

Mom's reaction was more eloquent.

"Well, aren't you the one, Pierre. Wonderful! Come on down and give me a hug."

Ed steadied the ladder as Pierre scrambled down.

Francine pulled away a little teary. She put her hands on his shoulders.

"We're gonna miss you very much."

"Ah, Frankie. Don't worry. I'm here now. Let's keep moving!"

Together, our quartet managed the impossible. The Granville Street FROG was ready for her debut with just three hours to spare.

The night was a success. Between us, my boss and I chatted to over 200 people, a handful of whom were curious passersby. It was marvelous. The reviews on the new location were overwhelmingly positive, and the multiple sales and "take home on approvals" made the exhausting three weeks all worth it.

We'd clearly parachuted into the heart of the action. Over the next few weeks, our foot traffic doubled, thanks in no small part to the world renown art gallery two doors down, and the heirloom jeweler and half a dozen quality antique shops across the street. Many of their customers expressed amazement that "the new girl on the block" had actually been in business for a decade.

However, it wasn't all about location. The previous year's Expo '86 also figured heavily. Held from May to October, the "Transportation and Communication: World in Motion" themed attraction drew over twenty-two million visitors. It literally introduced Vancouver to the world and when many attendees returned to the city a year later for a second, closer look, it was the serious antique collectors who found their way into our shop.

Our regulars waxed on about how everything showed so much better with space around it. While we weren't nearly as elegant as Bard's roomy Lantern Shop, at least we were no longer the cramped, chilly cousins. We still had to store some of the bigger pieces at Tolmie and at the farm, but there was much less need to schlep things out onto the sidewalk.

However, the modern conveniences of the shop were the true godsend. The underground parking lot meant we no longer had to sprint through the rain to get to our cars. The functioning heating enabled us to lose the layers, gloves and cozy scarves during winter. Yes, Peter, you were right. The $25,000 key money was worth it. And more.

CHAPTER 37

Taxing Issues

I was on holiday at my friend Melinda's lakeside cottage in Ontario when Francine called me in a right swivet.

"I've got a Canada Revenue Agency tax auditor coming by with a few questions tomorrow, Kelly. Some wretch must have turned us in."

I relaxed. No one had died.

"'A few questions' is not an audit, Mom. Just answer honestly. It's no big deal."

I was wrong. The auditor insisted on a second meeting; one with me, on my first day back. I began to worry, thinking about the sales we'd made involving customers who refused to pay the tax. In order to submit the correct sales tax to the government, I worked backwards to arrive at a sales figure that, combined with its appropriate sales tax, would come close to the amount the customer paid. Had some of the necessary adjustments been wrong? If so, how many?

I went in early on the day of the meeting, hoping for a few quiet moments over coffee. But someone was already huddled under our awning.

"I'm from Revenue Canada," he muttered, shooting out a cold hand.

"I'm from Frankie Robinson's. Welcome, welcome. Goodness, you're nice and early. How splendid. Come in, come in."

Mathew ducked ahead of me into the shop.

"Welcome back to Frankie Robinson Oriental Gallery!" I boomed, as if promoting a cleaning product on television. The man claimed the chair behind our office's large rosewood desk while I stumbled about flicking on lights and shutting off the alarm.

Mathew slumped over the desk and began massaging his temples. He looked exhausted. Perhaps this wouldn't be too bad, after all.

"Frankie will swoop in with coffee momentarily, Mathew," I purred. No response. I turned on the radio and Starship's peppy "Nothing's Gonna Stop Us Now" coursed throughout the room, which I chose to take as a further good sign.

"Shut it off! I can't think. I've been up all night with a 10-day-old baby," Mathew snapped. "Right. I need to see your last three months' worth of sales invoices."

Message received. This wasn't a social visit; I wasn't to ask about the newborn or indeed anything personal. I slapped down the three stacks of July, August and September invoices.

"Good Morning, Kel, welcome home! I've got coffee," Francine suddenly rang out.

"Excellent. Mathew and I can sure do with a cup!" I blurted, intent on forestalling unfortunate comments concerning the auditor's visit.

"Well, aren't you the early bird, Mathew? I'm sure Kelly is delighted to get started. I'll leave you two to sort through things. I'll just be out front."

Mathew sniffed as Francine escaped into the showroom. He

straightened his spine, downed some coffee and eased the paper-clip from the July invoice pile. I wrapped cold fingers around my mug as he familiarized himself with FROG's sales forms. After an insufferable hour of invoice flipping, I was about to suggest I join Francine when the auditor suddenly ran his hand along the length of the Chinese rosewood desk.

"Is this for sale, Kelly?"

"It surely is! Isn't the patina on it lovely? It's not an antique. We found it in a tiny shop in Macau ..."

The auditor's eyes locked onto mine. Their intensity could liquefy granite.

"The government considers it sold. You've effectively pulled it out of inventory by using it back here. Did you send in the tax on it?"

Of course we didn't send in the tax on it. It never occurred to me. I bolted for the showroom, bleating, "Let me check with Francine."

"You've got to be kidding, Kelly! It's bloody highway robbery!"

"Shh, he'll hear you, Mom."

"Well, God help him if he thinks I'm going to tolerate such ridiculous... ."

This blatant anger was concerning. If she rattled him, we could be here until Christmas. I tugged on her arm and pulled her out of earshot.

"God help *us* if you keep it up. Please. We don't want him demanding ten years' worth of sales slips. Can you please focus on selling while I deal with him? I do the books, I can answer his questions."

She studied me for a few seconds before reluctantly nodding.

"Fine. I'll be on sales and coffee detail. Go do your thing."

I crept back into the office to consult the inventory book for the desk's retail price.

"FROG owes you $210 on the desk," I announced, my voice annoyingly raspy.

The auditor removed the stubby pencil from behind his ear and officiously recorded that tidbit onto his notepad. I plopped back into my chair, silently fuming. If this guy thought he could force me into an attitude of humble servitude he was mistaken. I'd not intentionally done anything wrong. Nor had Francine.

Bless her. My mother managed to keep her side of our bargain. Her diary entry on the evening of the first day confirms she understood the brief. She wrote, "I hope I came across as an ass, a weird eccentric incapable of answering any financial questions."

Two hours into the second day, the moribund Mathew suddenly awoke, quivering like a dog anticipating breakfast.

"Kelly, please explain that!"

He tapped a slender index finger upon my barely legible "Paid with seven checks on the NNHE, final payment August 10th" scribble.

"The NNHE is our over-time-with-no-interest payment policy," I squeaked, launching into its salient qualities.

The auditor's disdain for the policy rivaled that of bookkeeper Jane's. However, when I didn't take the bait, he soldiered on, unearthing a few errors on my part and also on Francine's. He lost it after finding a fifth one.

"Do you two simply play with the sales tax whenever it suits?"

"Of course not," I snapped. "Look, we're doing our best here. The customers think they're getting away with it. Of course they aren't. They're just getting the item at a cheaper price and we make a sale. Win-win."

His response was irritatingly neutral. I simmered as he jotted down the latest amount owing and continued plowing through the August invoices.

Things perked up when a prominent television news reporter stopped by on the afternoon of Mathew's third day. A FROG newbie, it was important Francine acknowledge him correctly. The man's ego was notorious.

"Welcome to my shop. I see you came by cab. Where are you visiting from?"

Oh no. He'd be most offended she didn't recognize him. I ached to slip out onto the floor and shift conversational gears, but Mathew had me verbally tethered to the chair.

"Nowhere. I live here. I'm looking for something that can hide my television."

"Wonderful, I believe we have several good options. I do know my inventory. My degrees are in Oriental Art History, and before I opened this business a decade ago, I was a professor for eight years in the department of Fine Arts at UBC."

Good rising above it all, Sensei.

"We found this magnificent antique Chinese cabinet on our last trip to Hong Kong. It was created during that magical time when China's tea, silk and porcelain trade was flourishing. Note the simple, classic lines, typical of the Qing dynasty." The cabinet door creaked open. "Isn't it timeless? You'd never guess this piece is over 200 years old, now would you?"

Take that, Mathew. The Sensei might not fully understand bookkeeping but she certainly knew her business.

"Is it really over 200 years old? Wow. That's impressive. I do like it, Frankie, and the depth would easily hold our television. However, $3,000 is a bit more than I was hoping to spend." The fellow adopted a wheedling tone. "Could you possibly come down on the price?"

Mathew stirred beside me.

"You do love it, don't you? Okay, I could take off 10 percent which would bring it down to $2,700."

This would be Francine's largest sale during Mathew's visit.

"Thank you. Of course, I'm not going to pay the sales tax."

Mathew glanced at me, his head cocked.

"Oh, what timing!" Francine's voice was molten sugar. "Would you care to meet a Canada Revenue Agency taxman? We've got one inspecting our books right now. I know he'd be thrilled to educate you on the necessity of paying every penny of the sales tax."

A barely audible squeak precipitated the tinkling of the door chime. The reporter had left the building.

"Kelly, my purse."

Time for some retail therapy with Mrs. King.

We received the auditor's assessment that Halloween. It wasn't a treat. FROG's errors and accumulated fines were assessed at the ghastly sum of just under $20,000. Paul, our financial wizard, immediately filed a defense, and Mathew responded by asking for six months of additional sales slips. He wisely dealt with them offsite. The amended total came in at just over $10,000.

That hefty sum was a sobering catalyst. Going forward, all sales invoices were meticulously filled out and the taxes were paid in a timely manner.

We never did learn why Revenue Canada ordered the audit. Francine believes it was the act of another dealer who was jealous of our success. However, we were never able to prove it.

CHAPTER 38

Mystery Solved

A grueling 15K run through the steep residential streets of West Vancouver proved the perfect antidote to Mathew's sojourn. Held each October, the Khatsahlano run was organized by the owner of a small West Vancouver sportswear store. The sweatshirts awarded to the finishers were legendary.

This year's race was a wet one. I ran it alongside several of my pals from my YMCA marathon running clinic, as well as a friend visiting from New Zealand. Neville and I first met at our goddaughter's christening in Auckland, four years earlier.

After sloshing through puddles and mud for nearly two hours, we zipped home for a shower and dry clothes, before meeting up again for a celebratory brunch at the iconic Sylvia Hotel, one of Vancouver's original boutique hotels on the shores of English Bay. I recommended it, knowing Neville would enjoy the food as well as the spectacular ocean view.

I reluctantly squeezed into the seat wedged between the wall and a stranger. Starving, I didn't relish awkward conversation. However, things improved immeasurably as the fellow poured some wine into my glass and fired two powdery rolls onto my plate.

"You must be hungry, Kelly. Man, it was a wet one this morning, eh? Have you warmed up yet?"

My garbled affirmation unleashed a spew of soggy crumbs upon the pristine linen tablecloth which he discreetly mopped up.

"Don't worry, no need to talk. Just eat. I'm John, Carly's boyfriend. We met as ski patrollers up at Hollyburn Mountain. As you probably know, the patrollers help out with Khatsahlano every year. I was a route marshaller today, in charge of ensuring you all ran left instead of right."

As he flashed me a lopsided grin, I caught my fellow runner Carly's eye. Her dimples popped as she smiled back. John was a lucky man. His girlfriend was not only adventurous, but also very kind.

"How'd you become a ski patroller, John?" I managed between mouthfuls.

"I met up with some of the Hollyburn gang when I volunteered to search for that Mount Seymour hiker last summer. We didn't find the poor guy unfortunately, but they asked me to try out as a patroller. I did and now here we are. Oh, we need more wine."

He topped up our glasses just as the omelets arrived.

"You must know Mount Seymour pretty well, John," I asked, shoveling in a forkful.

"I do. I'm familiar with all of the North Shore Mountains, actually. I've hiked them since I was a little guy."

Interesting.

We ate in companionable silence until I felt somewhat better.

"So where are you from, John?"

I was curious as few of my friends were born in Vancouver.

"Here. In Vancouver. At St. Paul's Hospital."

My fork clattered onto the plate. He was born in the same

hospital as me. What else did we have in common? My food now quite forgotten, I began to pepper John with questions. It was fun to learn how like mine, his family was important to him, they had a cabin on the Sunshine Coast and were also dog people. By the time dessert arrived I was of the opinion Carly was the lucky one; this fellow was quite a guy. My spidey sense was also on full alert. We'd surely met before, but when?

"So, what do you do when you're not skiing or hiking, John?"

"I work with my dad in his house construction business, mostly doing large renovations. We renovated that Shaughnessy designer show home a few years ago. You probably had some pieces there."

The back of my neck began to tingle.

I whispered, "What's your last name, John?"

"McKenzie."

"Margaret McKenzie is your mom?"

He nodded and smiled.

"Yes, last time I checked."

Good Lord. It was him. The guy who got my lovely little pig before I finished paying for it, some four years ago now.

I settled back in my chair, pleased to finally learn the truth. Mrs. McKenzie's son was not only well and thriving, he was indeed worthy of my lovely little pig.

CHAPTER 39

A Narrow Miss

"**K**elly, come quick. I've been attacked by a reindeer!"
I raced to the shop and found Francine hunkered down in the office with a wad of paper towel clamped over her right eye. Thank God it wasn't blood soaked.

"We have to leave immediately. Dr. Fitzgibbon's receptionist said he'll see me as soon as I can get there."

My mother is known for her icy focus in an emergency and today was no exception. Of course, she'd already called her eye doc and applied first aid. I slapped a note on the door alerting folks that FROG was closing early, and helped her up from the chair.

"Shall we refresh the paper towel, Mom?"

"God, no! Only the doctor will be going near my eye! Or what's left of it."

Not quite the update one wants from their mother.

We didn't speak again until I had her safely ensconced in the car.

"I was reaching for a book when the reindeer suddenly toppled head first off the top of the bookshelf. It might have knocked me out for a moment or two," Francine added, *sotto voce*.

Jesus. There could be serious damage under that paper bundle. The reindeer was heavier than a 10-pound bag of sugar and blessed with sizable, pointy-tipped antlers.

When we stumbled into a waiting room more crowded than a celebrity wedding, I realized most of the patients would have waited months for today's appointment. Francine's emergency would bump some unfortunates further down the line.

The young woman seated behind the desk didn't seem fazed by my mother's appearance, which comforted me. She'd seen a lot worse.

"Name?"

Francine pushed past me.

"No one is touching my paper towel except the doctor. I don't know if I still have an eye."

Time to intercede.

"Hi. This is Frankie Robinson. She called a few minutes ago about being bonked on the head by a reindeer and you were kind enough to fit her in." I lowered my voice and leaned in closer. "She's not quite herself."

The curiosity in the room ramped up exponentially. My concussed companion had survived a battle with a wild animal. Dr. Fitzgibbon emerged from his office, sporting some serious headgear.

"Frankie! Do come in and we'll get you sorted."

I slumped with relief into a chair.

When they emerged from his office fifteen minutes later, Francine's sprightly steps spoke volumes.

She gingerly gestured toward the impressive bandage now covering a third of her face.

"Your mother is one lucky woman, dear. Another quarter of an inch and she'd have been in *serious* trouble." The doctor gripped her shoulders. "Now remember, Frankie. I don't want you going into work tomorrow. You need to rest." He addressed me once again. "She can book her follow-up appointment once she's home."

Francine showered him with thanks, and after gracing the room with a regal nod, sailed out.

The ride to Tolmie Street was illuminating.

"Someone up there is looking after me, Kel. Truly. The damn animal just hurled itself off the shelf. There's a small gash below the eye but I don't need stitches, thank God. Dr. Fitzgibbon has the bedside manner of an angel. The worst part was anticipating the removal of the paper towel. However, he handled that beautifully by distracting me with a cute story about his daughter. I forgot the reason for the visit. What a relief! I had visions of going around like a pirate sporting an eye patch for the rest of my days. I'm to ice it with a bag of frozen peas. I wonder if we have some at home. Probably not. Do you think a Ziplock bag of frozen strawberries would be okay? We've got plenty of those from the farm …"

Francine reported for duty just two days later. Her puffy, multi-hued eye was a true showstopper and of course everyone wanted to know how it happened. We encouraged them to guess but no one ever got it right.

CHAPTER 40

Christmas Miracles

A brisk wind whistled through my thin cardigan and I huddled closer to Francine. We were on the sidewalk studying my latest window dressing efforts.

"It's perfect. I wouldn't change a thing, Kel," Francine decreed.

Great. I was learning.

My first attempt four years ago wasn't quite as successful. However, Francine handled it masterfully.

"A boudoir theme? How original! Your use of the chairs and the kimonos is really clever, Kel," she observed, her face blank. "Hmm. Can we try losing some chairs? I'm thinking one might be stronger than six. Good. Now, maybe you could select just one special kimono from your pile. Oh, I do like that. Nice. Okay, now just drape it casually over the chair's arm and let it pool onto the floor. Yes, I think that's more impactful, don't you?"

I did.

My windows only began to truly sing when I grasped Francine's ultimate goal for this important eye into the shop. Each display should infer that no matter your budget, you were always welcome at FROG. This was achieved by the inclusion of both the exquisite, high-end pieces and the quirky, cheap and cheerful. As my design eye slowly matured, I found myself also adding pops of humor. It turned out that safe, vanilla windows did nothing for me. Thankfully, my boss felt the same.

Today's festive efforts featured Francine's recalcitrant reindeer and a pair of equally top-heavy siblings. Tethered together with red satin ribbons, they soared majestically skywards, thanks to three different sized cardboard boxes hiding under a bolt of fluffy white fabric.

A large, cedar *Kuruma-dansu* (wheeled tansu) flanked by two smaller heavily armored *funa-dansu* (sea chests), were the current backdrop for the reindeers' ascension. They each sported a life-size, black-and-white papier mache penguin. In an effort to lend some authentic perspective to the height of the flight path, I'd scattered several inexpensive, exquisitely hand-carved, wooden roosters, chickens and pigs about the base.

Our window platform was so deep that no amount of tweaking would allow the contents to shine without a colorful backdrop. I solved that problem today with the help of a 200-year-old, two-panel gold leaf Japanese screen. Santa's reindeer were winging off into a night sky graced with a silver moon and a pair of red-crested white cranes.

The plan was for the trio to anchor our festive window from late November until Christmas Eve, accompanied by an ever-changing tableau. The reindeer weren't for sale. We decided to hang on to them despite their ability to inflict grievous injury.

The window dressed, we moved on to cards. Francine's design for this year's festive card featured a sprightly, life-sized, jade green frog sporting a rakishly-tilted, red and gold crown. When our printers advised us it would be much cheaper to produce in black and white, I foolishly volunteered to be the chief colorist for all 300.

A customer in his late 60s with pixie-like features dropped in when I was working on the first 50 cards. I barely acknowledged him as I was feeling a bit rough. I'd been coloring for two hours and a nagging headache had blossomed into nausea.

I was annoyed with myself when the chap suddenly left the shop without a word. I should have focused on him more, the damn cards could wait. It was only November, after all.

When he returned twenty minutes later, I leapt up to greet him.

"Welcome back. I'm sorry if I didn't make you feel welcome before," I groveled, pathetically.

He smiled and shoved a white bag into my hand.

He was giving me a gift? I blushed and peeked inside. Clocking my obvious confusion, he rushed to explain.

"They're scentless felt pens. I had to replace your toxic ones. This place smells like a glue factory. I felt woozy after just five minutes."

"Thank you! How thoughtful. I bet that's why I feel sick. Gosh, it never occurred to me to blame the felt pens! I didn't even know they came scentless."

As I swept an emerald green one over the frog's bulbous eyes, the fellow smiled.

"I'm glad to help. Get well and have a very Merry Christmas."

With that, the anonymous felt-pen elf slipped away, never to return.

The next Saturday, a tanned male in his late 30s, rushed in to ask the price of the reindeer.

He was disappointed to learn they weren't for sale.

"You wouldn't want them. Honestly, they're evil," I giggled, before launching into the story of Francine's endangered eye.

"Well, aren't you blessed to work with your mother," he whispered when I finished. "I'd *love* to work with my mother. She's an extraordinary woman." He looked directly at Francine. "Now, I'm assuming you didn't name the shop after your daughter. You must be Frankie, I'm Harold Smith," the fellow ventured, sticking out his hand.

Harold went on to share that his elderly mother still lived in the family home in Burnaby, on the outskirts of Vancouver.

"My husband was born in Burnaby!" Francine exclaimed.

We were golden from then on.

Harold admitted he was having trouble finding a unique coffee table base. His partner was picky. We showed him several options and he seemed particularly taken with the pair of crouching, life-sized wooden ibexes we'd sourced in northern Thailand. The matte black bodies were three-feet long. Their crowning features were a pair of magnificent golden horns that arched grandly backwards from the top of their heads to halfway down their backs.

"We've only got the two, Harold," Francine cautioned. "I wanted to buy at least six, but Kelly insisted that while a lone pair is special, multiples are not."

To be honest, I doubted that we could move several pairs. These specimens were more suited for the grand lobby of a hotel, rather than a home.

"'Less is more,' Harold. If Francine's said it to me once, she's said it a thousand times," I explained with a smile.

"Oh, you two are adorable!" he chortled, promising to return soon.

Seamus came in with him the following Saturday.

We stood back as they slowly circled the ibexes.

"I've never seen anything like them," Seamus muttered quietly. "A top *could* easily rest upon the horns. Your suggestion of a sheet of smoky glass is brilliant, Frankie. Let's measure them, Harold."

"Oh seriously, fellas, please just hurl them into your car and take them home. It's the quickest way to know if they'll actually work," I insisted with Francine nodding in agreement.

The astonished couple lugged the heavy creatures out in two trips. It took a bit of juggling, however, they finally managed to wedge one ibex into the trunk and the other onto the backseat of their red Toyota Corolla.

Harold returned with a check later that afternoon.

"We're thrilled! They're absolutely perfect. You've got to see them. Can you join us for tea tomorrow afternoon?"

These guys worked fast. The golden horns already sported a sheet of thick smoky glass when Francine and I stopped by. The ibexes couldn't be more perfect in this immaculate, highly sophisticated space.

"Your place makes me want to rush home and toss out half my stuff," I confessed.

Harold nodded in agreement.

"I get it. I told you my mom still lives in the house I grew up in, right? Well, it's 'Clutter Central.' She keeps everything. My three siblings and I are convinced she's still got all of our kindergarten artwork! She'd be horrified to learn we gave our old coffee table to our downstairs neighbors, wouldn't she, Seamus?"

"Very much so. You should see her house! Who knows, maybe one day you will."

Francine and I just smiled, knowing that would never happen. We couldn't be more wrong.

CHAPTER 41

Christmas Crackers

When Bette phoned in late November with the unfortunate news that Bard had succumbed to his bone and prostate cancer battle, Francine immediately asked her to join us for Christmas. While she was delighted that the widow accepted, I wasn't. How could we merrily tear into gifts in the presence of a grieving octogenarian?

However, Bette proved to be just as I remembered from the cockroach nightmare. Plump, powdered and pleasant. It looked like we'd be spared any awkwardness this Christmas season, after all.

What a relief.

We gathered at my sister's just after lunch on Christmas Day and spent a pleasant afternoon opening presents. Wendy was announcing dinner when we suddenly heard giggles coming from the hallway. Five-year-old twins Ashley and Chelsea lurched into the living room, dragging a large dark green suitcase wrapped with an enormous shiny red bow. My heart ached for the innocent who was about to be thrust into the spotlight.

Francine leapt to her feet and cheerfully chirped, "Merry Christmas, Kel!"

Oh, please, no.

A panicked scan of the room revealed that only the girls, my parents, and Bette, were in on it. The seventeen others, a mix of visiting relatives and friends, were understandably annoyed that their turkey feast was going to be delayed.

I slapped on a smile more rictus than joyful and began to unzip the suitcase. My heart sank. The suspiciously thick envelope tucked inside cried out for a public viewing.

"You leave for Tokyo in 10 days!" Francine shrieked in her best Oprah imitation.

I immediately burst into tears.

The room went sub-Arctic and Francine scrambled admirably.

"Oh, Kel, darling, please don't be upset. The shop and I will be fine! I'm so excited for you. You'll be staying with Pierre. He can't wait to see you."

Bless her. My mother had absolutely no idea that I wasn't upset about leaving her in the lurch. I was crying out of pure relief. This gift meant a reprieve from Carly's blissful stories of her adventures with John. My opinion of her boyfriend had only improved with each subsequent encounter. The truth was, I liked John. A lot. The sooner I was able to escape the happy couple, the better.

My sister handed me some tissues and I struggled to compose myself.

"How generous, Mom. Thank you! Let's chat about it later, I'm sure the troops are starved. Let's eat!" I hollered, fooling no one but myself.

With everyone now happily tucking into their meals, my thoughts shifted into bookkeeper mode. This Japanese sojourn was going to cost FROG a hefty sum. Could I contribute somehow? I thought of the several customers who regularly shared their lengthy wishlists of Japanese antiquities. Among the highlights

NEVER, NEVER, HARDLY EVER

were lacquered boxes and bowls, small bronze hand mirrors, tiny *netsuke* (carved toggles used to attach something like a tobacco pouch to an obi) and *inro* (the containers attached to the netsuke), *yukata* (cotton robes) and obis, and decorative scrolls. Maybe I could mitigate the financial hit by tracking down these smaller items and schlepping them home in my suitcase. Surely we could resell them at a decent price without the added costs of shipping fees. I liked it. The concept left me sparkling with a positive energy I'd not felt since meeting John all those weeks earlier.

The good vibes continued. When Godfrey and Francine invited me to dinner at a local restaurant the next day, I happily accepted, and even encouraged them to tag along beforehand to an after-noon Boxing Day drop-in at the home of two FROG regulars. I was confident that an additional three guests wouldn't upset Ted, an Air New Zealand ticket agent, and Dave, a part-time caterer.

It was difficult not to giggle when Bette moseyed outside wrapped in Francine's full-length beaver fur coat. The octogenarian looked well chuffed, as if she was heading out to her movie premiere. Francine's quick shake of the head told me all I needed to know. Their guest cared little for the rising popularity of animal rights groups like PETA and had scorned my mother's faux fur option. God only knew how this would be received by the other guests. We'd have to somehow slip the old gal in unnoticed.

No one responded to our knocking. I tried the handle and the front door swung open, revealing two rooms: a large living room and a tiny dining room. Both were packed with chatty, thirsty guests. Very few were older than me. Perhaps I should have come alone.

My mother strode off through the crowd like a ship homing into a berth, while Bette confidently prepped for her grand entrance. I watched numbly as she reapplied her lipstick and fluffed up the fur's collar. She batted away Godfrey's proffered hand as Ted welcomed us with open arms.

"Kelly! You brought an entourage. We couldn't be more delighted. Come in, come in!"

My feverish explanation of the aged-plus-three was abruptly interrupted by a shriek, and then a sickening thump. Dear God, Bette. She'd stumbled on the raised threshold and was now sprawled face down on the thick Turkish carpet, her arms and legs all akimbo as if in flight. I prayed for no shattered bones.

Ted was the first to react.

"Are you alright, Hon?" he asked anxiously.

Bette's muffled yet eloquent response was one for the books.

"I'm very well, thank you. And you?"

As she continued to remain prone, Godfrey ran a swift verbal assessment, grilling her about the condition of her knees, wrists and hands. When she insisted that nothing hurt, I offered up a silent thanks for the cushioning features of the fur coat, and lurched into a round of introductions.

"Ted, this is our dear Hawaiian friend Bette. She's recently widowed and grieving from the island of Oahu. Bette, this is host Ted. He's the airline rep, not the food genius."

Godfrey grinned at my garbled efforts and nodded at Ted. The room held its collective breath as the two gingerly tipped the dazed woman onto her back.

"No, up, up!" she stridently protested.

They grasped her by the elbows and hefted her slowly onto her feet. No one spoke as Bette swayed for a second or two before tottering over to the closest chair. Her forehead was odd. I peered closer and was alarmed to spot a burgeoning lump above her left brow. Godfrey, concerned that the poor woman might be concussed, discretely asked her to track his forefinger with her eyes.

When he finally relaxed his hand, the relief in the room was undeniable.

"That was quite the performance, Bette. What are your plans for an encore?"

She fluttered her eyes and smiled coquettishly.

"Oh, my dear, Geoff, one can only ponder that over a glass of chilled white wine ..."

It was impossible not to fixate on Bette. Feeling the warmth of the crowded room, she stretched expansively and began to unbutton the coat. It sprang open, revealing a vision even more disconcerting than her facial lump. Bette's elegant black midi dress was now bunched halfway up her plump thigh, exposing a pair of mistreated knees. Fiery red and swollen, the excessive flesh mushroomed over top of a pair of restrictive nylon knee highs. The nylon torture traps were definitely a recent acquisition. Bard would have been appalled at such a sartorial shortcut. I couldn't tear my eyes away.

Alerted by Godfrey's smothered chortle, Bette swiftly drew the coat back over her knees. After several restorative sips of Chablis, she threw back her shoulders and cast her eyes imperiously about the room. The old gal was clearly more capable than I thought.

There wasn't a hope in hell for any semblance of normality though. Not with her forehead lump now surpassing that of Francine's reindeer bonk. It was as if the octogenarian had ingested a golf ball and it tunneled a path to her forehead. The effect was most unsettling. Indeed, when Bette inadvertently beamed it in the direction of the young man opposite her, he blanched and bolted. My heart melted. Not only had the woman just lost her husband, but also all of this current awkwardness and discomfort was my fault. She'd be fine, if not for me. I pledged to be kinder.

My wrist was suddenly gripped in a vice-like hold and Bette's warm breath hissed in my ear, "Kelly, someone's stolen my purse!"

Surely I'd misheard.

No. The clenching continued, forcing me to act.

"Oh, I'm sure it's here somewhere, Bette," I heartily replied in an attempt to jolly her out of it. I dropped to the floor on my hands and knees, but she wasn't to be dissuaded.

"Kelly, I can see that it's gone. You're wasting time. We need to alert the authorities. *NOW!*"

Conversation once again skidded to a dead halt and my scalp tingled under the piercing attention. I looked for my parents but the room was too crowded. Fortunately, Dave dashed over to help.

"Happy Boxing Day, Dave! Thank you so very much for the invitation. Goodness me, you won't soon forget our entrance! This is our good widow Bette, who is grieving with us over Christmas. She's from Oahu. Bette this is Dave, the other half of our Boxing hosts."

Dave ignored my unfortunate introduction by gently grasping Bette's hand. She glared at him, flashing her bulbous forehead.

"One of your friends has stolen my purse!"

Poor Dave was now thoroughly confused. Not only had the party crasher taken a dreadful tumble, but also she was accusing one of their own of theft! Any help from me was hopeless. I couldn't even remember what the damn thing looked like. As Bette trumpeted the egregious claim yet again, I became aware of ill-concealed snickers. People were beginning to believe that the old gal was truly crackers. It was time to bring in Francine.

"Frankie, Bette needs you!" I sang out shrilly.

Francine melted out of the crowd.

"What lovely friends you have, Dave! I love how they appreciate the kitchen tansu," she exclaimed, referring to the couple's most recent FROG purchase. She squeezed his arm and turned to Bette.

"Now, my dear, how can I help? Oh, my goodness. It must have been quite the tumble. What a relief you're okay." Her voice dropped to a murmur. "Can someone get her some ice?"

Dave headed for the freezer while Bette stared down my mother as she would a naughty child.

"I don't care for ice with my Chablis, thank you, and I'm most certainly *not* okay, Frankie. Someone has stolen my purse!" She clutched the fur coat tightly about her neck. "Thank goodness I didn't take this off. You'd never have seen it again."

My mother hesitated, deep in thought, before breaking out into the broadest of smiles.

"No, your purse is fine. Remember we decided it was best to leave it at home? It's safely waiting for you at the foot of your bed. Now, then, while we wait for Dave to return with the ice, perhaps you'd top up our drinks, Kel?"

I grabbed their glasses and escaped to the kitchen.

CHAPTER 42

Presents of Mind

Francine's generous Christmas gift sparked a healthy perspective. It was time to push the reset button on the Carly and John front. Still early days for the couple, they needed to work out whether they were a fit and I needed to create my own magical memories.

The good karma gods were smiling going forward. I was bumped up to Business Class on the wide-body Boeing 747 bound for Narita. What a treat. I skipped up the circular staircase and took full advantage of the ten hours of solid pampering.

Pierre was waiting for me at Arrivals. I grinned as he staggered under the weight of my two heavy suitcases.

"Francine's to blame, Pierre. She gave me several bottles of Johnny Walker Black to hand out as gifts here."

"Very wise. There's a real art to gift-giving here, Kel. You'll see."

After living in Japan for close to a year, our French Canadian friend now spoke Japanese well. At least I thought so. The uniformed attendants at the various traffic stops along the route to his apartment would only speak to him in English. Something Pierre accepted with grace.

"Some folks can't see beyond my Caucasian face, Kelly. It has them instantly assuming that I can't speak Japanese. You just get used to it."

His apartment, located in the heart of Sendai, was about half the size of our 10th Avenue shop. It boasted a pocket-sized kitchen on the right, a tiny bathroom on the left and a rectangular room in the middle which would serve as our dining/living quarters during the day and our bedroom at night.

Pierre used the space well. Every stick of furniture was multifunctional. He'd wedged the largest piece into the kitchen. The Victorian oak armoire housed not only his clothing and dishes, but also several of his newly acquired Japanese antiques. It was like old times watching him run his hands over a stack of carefully folded yukatas and obis.

"I'm buying only quality pieces, Kelly, ones that I might sell when I get back to Vancouver."

I didn't share *my* purchasing plans with him. That could wait.

The central room was "two-mat-sized." The bedtime tatami mats took up the entire floor space. Once he'd laid out the futons and duvets, Pierre offered me the set closest to the bathroom. Of course he did. He'd witnessed me tripping over many an innocent object back home.

I was grateful that tomorrow was a school day and that Pierre was happy to settle in early. Awake for over 24 hours, I was "dizzy with exhaustion," as Francine would say. I crawled under the thick duvet and relaxed into the futon.

"Sweet dreams, Kelly. Don't try anything funny. I certainly won't," Pierre intoned in mock seriousness.

We dissolved into giggles, and the joy of being on a fresh adventure swept over me. Francine couldn't have given me a better gift. I drifted off to sleep happier than I'd been in weeks.

The room was freezing when we woke up. Pierre leapt out of bed and primed the ancient portable gas heater. We continued to be up close and personal, with my roommate prepping for his morning ablutions in front of the full-length mirror mounted on the back of the armoire door. There were no other sensible options. As Godfrey would say, "you couldn't swing a cat" in the tiny bathroom, and I wouldn't hear of Pierre attempting it in the frigid communal hallway.

After a quick change in the bathroom, Pierre began lathering up the shaving soap with a boar bristle brush. He then spread the foam over his neck and chin before carefully scraping it off with an ivory-handled safety razor. As he wiped away the residue and gave his mustache a quick trim, I assumed he was done. But no. The man dove into the armoire and fished out a handful of tubes and bottles, and began efficiently applying their mysterious contents to different areas of his face. This was followed by a swift massaging of his cheekbones, chin and neck. A relaxing moment under a damp towel and a spritz of a little mousse in his hair, and my host was ready for breakfast. The whole scenario was a game changer; I'd definitely be asking him for a skin product consult while I was here.

I hung around Sendai for the first week, adjusting to the time change and becoming familiar with Pierre's neighborhood. It was impressive watching him converse with the local shopkeepers in rapid-fire Japanese. They clearly had no problem understanding him.

Pierre stopped asking me about culture shock by the second day. My nattering on about how I felt "instantly at home in Japan" must have been insufferable. But I did find the transition seamless. The Sendai weather, chilly and damp, was similar to Vancouver's. The food was also familiar. Already a big fan of sushi, tempura and everything miso, I was open to sampling anything my host recommended.

Of course, working at FROG definitely helped with the quick acclimation. We carried the lacquer bowls, spoons, and trays found in the restaurants, as well as the scrolls and woodblock prints on offer in the neighborhood galleries. We also sold tansu that would have originally stored futons like the one I currently slept on. I honestly felt as if I was among old friends.

What a fool.

I was oblivious to a unique form of "reverse culture shock" that was about to slam in with the force of a tsunami.

Pierre and I were invited to dinner at a local restaurant by the family of two of his students. The invitation included drinks at their place first. I was excited. It would be a treat to see Japanese antiquites being used in their country of origin.

Unfortunately, we got off to a rather dodgy start. My over-sized, fiery orange sweater emboldened with a giant Picasso-like beaded female face couldn't be more inappropriate. Mrs. Yamamoto's white lace blouse, red cashmere cardigan and gray slacks meshed nicely with her husband's soft gray turtleneck sweater and crisp black pants. I was all carnival clown to their understated elegance.

Their home decor was nothing like I was expecting. It was as if I'd parachuted into a contemporary Canadian furniture showroom; all modern wooden cabinets, leather sofas and glass table tops. My five-year-old nephew and nieces were older than any piece here.

Desperate to conceal my disappointment, I awkwardly thrust the bottle of Johnny Walker at Mrs. Yamamoto. She took a peek inside the brown paper bag and passed it to her husband. His glance was even briefer.

Perhaps Francine was wrong about the universal popularity of Johnny Walker Black.

Matters weren't helped by Pierre's odd behavior. He seemed very subdued, almost obsequious in their presence. I took a large gulp of my wine and was about to inquire after their two sons, when Mrs. Yamamoto requested that we follow her into the dining room.

Their teak dining table boasted an assortment of beautifully wrapped gifts. When I glared at Pierre for neglecting to share that we were celebrating someone's birthday, he quickly shook his head. They were all for me. The disparity in the optics couldn't be more obvious. An uninspired token presented it in a tatty bag versus a wealth of artfully wrapped treasures.

Could this get any more awkward? Oh, yes. The couple's two teenage sons chose this moment to slip into the room and bow to Pierre, addressing their teacher formally as "Sensei." As they dutifully lined up with everyone on the opposite side of the table, it was the "let's watch the Canadians eat Chiang Mai takeout" all over again.

I called upon the strength that got me through that mystery meat special and blindly grabbed the nearest present. Mrs. Yamamoto spoke softly in Japanese.

"My wife says you make a lovely couple," Mr. Yamamoto smoothly translated as his sons chortled like the schoolboys they were.

They didn't know Pierre was gay? Why not? He was always so open about it at home, it never occurred to me that he wouldn't be here. He must have a very good reason. I thought back to the several examples of the antique Japanese *shunga* woodblock prints we carried at FROG. They featured graphic images of sexual activity. I assumed things were as liberal here on the gay front as at home, but maybe they weren't.

I was suddenly plunged back into the play-acting world of the adoring girlfriend, attending Christmas parties and Monster Truck rallies. But without a safety net. I wasn't prepared in the least. Why couldn't Pierre have given me some advance warning? I tried to catch his eye but he refused to look at me.

I tore into the beautiful handmade paper. Pierre gasped and his piercing blue eyes flashed a warning like the check engine light on my dashboard. I was to stop the intolerable rudeness, and slow down and appreciate the art of gift presentation, Japanese style. My soul seized in embarrassment. I was now officially the rude, stingy Canadian girlfriend in the loud sweater.

Excellent.

That and the sight of Pierre's handsome face, now a disturbing puce, forced me into a bit of a rethink. I'd be going back to normal life in just under three weeks while he was here, living a lie, for at least another year. Damn. It was time to get my act together. I could do this. It wouldn't be my first rodeo as the designated girlfriend, after all.

Signaling my allegiance, I squeezed his hand and slapped on a loving smile. Now channeling my inner geisha's apprentice or *maiko*, I slowly unfurled the rest of the paper. The pair of gold and persimmon lacquered chopsticks were exquisite.

"What a work of art!" I demurely exclaimed before bowing deeply to Mrs. Yamamoto and then to her husband. Pierre exhaled gratefully. Mollified, I smoothed out the tortured gift wrap, creased it tidily along the folds and awaited for the go-ahead to pluck up another package. I unwrapped each of the five other gifts at a slug's pace. It must have been like watching paint dry.

"Excuse me, we should depart soon if we're to make that dinner reservation," Mr. Yamamoto advised after patiently enduring my abrupt behavioral transformation.

"Yes, just one more." Using both hands, Mrs. Yamamoto presented me with an elegant ivory-colored silk bag decorated with soaring red-crested cranes. Noting my confusion, she spread it open.

"It's for the others," she instructed as if I was her third child. In went the lacquered chopsticks, followed by the white porcelain chopstick rest, the delicate gold paper fan, the pair of blue and white porcelain sake cups, the white *tabi* (socks with a separate area for the big toe), and the gorgeous silk scarf, which, as my hostess carefully stressed, could also be used to wrap a present. Pierre scooped up the bag, gallantly offered his arm and, as everyone smiled in approval, we headed as one to the car.

The positive uptick continued once we hit the restaurant. Constructed in the shape of a thick timbered pagoda, it was surrounded by a water-filled moat. After crossing over the tiny arched bridge, we were led to our shoji screened private room, where I managed to redeem myself perhaps a little more by swiftly removing my shoes and sinking to the cushions by the low table. I offered up silent thanks to my parents and our family go-to, *The Bamboo Terrace Chinese Restaurant* for introducing me to chopsticks before I was five.

The slightly chilled sake was delicious, as were the endless platters of *unangi* (eel), the house special. With the conversation now flowing mostly between the men, I was able to sit quietly in the shadows, sip my drink and pick through the threads of this emotional rollercoaster of an evening.

What a wake-up call. I'd constructed a totally false narrative about Japan while Pierre was grappling with real, unfathomable challenges that would likely continue throughout his stay. I topped up his sake and raised my cup to him in salute. The ever-observant

Mrs. Yamamoto smiled warmly, signaling her approval. Perhaps there was hope for dear Sensei's girlfriend after all.

CHAPTER 43

Two Decidedly
Different Offers

Should the teaching gig not work out and he opted not to become an antiques dealer, Pierre could always consider the travel biz. My host drew up an impressive itinerary for my second week in Japan. I was to travel 900 miles by ferry and train from the northern coastal town of Akita down to the southern hot springs town of Beppu. My travel buddy? Pierre's dog-eared *Fodor's Japan* book. I was to study up on the iconic highlights dotted along the route.

He laughed when I asked about pre-booking accommodation.

"If you want the true Japanese experience, Kelly, you have to stay at the *ryokan*s, or inns. All of your train stations have a travel office. Go there and ask the staff to book you in at the closest ryokan. It's easy. There's no need for any pre-booking."

It proved to be an effective system. The ryokans were always nearby, their rooms clean and cozy. Each private room contained a tatami mat, a thick futon and a television. Most also provided a yukata for the short stroll to the communal bathroom. Once night fell, I'd change into my pajamas, plug a fistul of yen into the television's coin box and tune into the game show channel. The shows were colorful. Competitors splashed, charged and rolled through challenging obstacle courses. My lack of Japanese didn't matter in the least. It was the perfect backdrop for reading up on the next day's plans.

When my train pulled into the station of a small village at 9:30 p.m. on the fourth day, I hot-footed it to the travel office. The agent spoke minimal English, but we persevered and I was confident she understood my request.

However, when there was still no sign of the ryokan after twenty minutes, I began to have my doubts. I was about to slosh back in the pouring rain for another consultation when someone called out from across the street, "Do you need help? I have English."

At my emphatic nod, the fellow darted over. In his mid-50s, he sported a tan bucket hat and a pair of spotless running shoes. He could have been out for a run but the dark trench coat and umbrella inferred he wasn't.

"Am I anywhere near this ryokan?" I asked, holding out the limp paper for him to peer at under the streetlight. He studied it carefully before nodding.

"Yes, you just need to continue going straight for the next two blocks and then make a sharp right turn. It'll be there on your left."

"That's fantastic. Thank you for noticing me," I gushed. Flicking my dripping hair out of my eyes, I smiled, shook his hand, shoved my duffel bag onto my shoulder and strode confidently up the street.

Footsteps splattered up behind me after only a block.

"Excuse me, Miss."

My heart sank. Had he gotten it wrong? Would I have to slog all the way back to the station?

He doffed his hat as I turned around.

"I will perform masturbation. You watch. I pay."

Good God.

I stared at the man, utterly gobsmacked. His face, both ernest and hopeful, confirmed that yes, I had heard him correctly.

"*Nooooo!*"

My response, the decibel equivalent of a troupe of male howler monkeys at full throttle, burned my throat. It felt as if I'd downed battery acid. The guttural riposte proved effective though. He made no attempt to follow me as I flew up the road.

My head buzzed. Bucket Hat Man looked so normal, but then again, so did Ted Bundy. Had he been stalking me from the station? What was with those squeaky clean running shoes? Were they worn to ensure speedy encroachment upon unsuspecting women? Oh God. Had he actually given me directions to his *house?*

Salvation loomed just a minute later. My ryokan. Right where he said it would be. I rocketed into the lobby to find the innkeeper nodding off behind a large desk. The woman was ancient, hard of hearing and spoke no English. There was no point in attempting to enlighten her about the extraordinary proposition. I grabbed the key and bolted to my room. After pushing my bag up against the locked sliding door, I threw myself upon the thick futon and lay there, gasping. I gradually gained a healthier perspective. It was only a verbal proposition. He didn't touch me. I was now safely under the protection of a seasoned octogenarian.

Sleep remained elusive. Did my foreignness and grateful exuberancy trigger the bizarre proposal? Or was this his nightly modus operandi? I suspected the former but wasn't going back for confirmation. As the ryokan settled into sleep and no one whispered salacious suggestions outside the door, my perspective gradually shifted from shock and uneasiness to one of grudging amusement. You couldn't fault his sentence structure. Francine's grinning face suddenly loomed in the darkness. I finally drifted off to sleep comforted by the undeniable joy she'd get from this little adventure.

⟨───⟩

"Do you need help? I have English."

Christ. It was the exact same wording of two nights earlier.

I slouched lower in my train seat and hid behind the Japan Railways station map. My fellow passenger looked harmless, but so did Bucket Hat Man. I chose to ignore the comment, hoping to imply that I didn't speak a lick of English.

However, I was in a bit of a pickle. My connecting train to Kyoto departed a mere three minutes after this one arrived. I needed clear directions to the departure platform if I had a hope in hell of making it. Unfortunately the only female prospect was sound asleep, her head lolling against the headrest.

"I'm also going to Kyoto today. I would be happy to ensure that you get on the right train. It can be rather tricky," my seatmate chirped.

Was the man clairvoyant? As I reluctantly lowered the map, he gestured towards my "Kyoto In A Day" pamphlet languishing on the seat beside me. Damn.

"Are you Canadian? I delivered a paper in Toronto. My profession is Mathematics."

The fact that he didn't assume I was American was intriguing. I studied him closer. This thin, tall gentleman with the silver streaks threaded throughout his black hair was the spitting image of TV's Mr. Rogers. I decided to give him a chance. There was plenty of opportunity to escape to another car if need be.

"May I show you this photo of my wife and our two sons? It was taken when we were in Florida last year."

It would be churlish not to look. I leaned closer. The happy trio were sitting at an oceanside table, the picture of normalcy. All three possessed honest, open faces.

"Our youngest is 16 and his brother is 19. However, I suspect that my wife would prefer that I didn't reveal her age."

That got me grinning.

"I'm lecturing tomorrow at a college. What brings you to Kyoto? Or perhaps, the better question is, what brings you to Japan?" he asked pleasantly.

Mr. Kamei was a good listener. Fully intrigued by my interest in Asian antiques, he asked intelligent questions and the half hour passed quickly without any awkward propositions. I had no reservations following him when it came time to detrain. He marched along the tracks with divine purpose and we made it onto the correct train with a full minute to spare. Perhaps thinking I'd like some time to myself, he elected to sit in a different carriage. But not without first handing me his card.

"Please call me at your convenience and we can arrange a time to get together for dinner. I know my wife would enjoy meeting you."

That was an offer I welcomed. I might just do it.

CHAPTER 44

Channeling Francine

With just over a week remaining, it was time to get serious about trying to pay for this trip. However, I wasn't confident I could pull it off. Francine wasn't even aware of this little gambit. It would be my first real solo buying experience. Without her guidance, I felt directionless, like a disabled boat helplessly bobbing about on stormy seas.

"Well, never mind. There's always the Bucket Hat Man option, Kel. You've got guaranteed earning potential there," Pierre teased with a grin.

I swatted him with the dishrag.

"No? Not tempted? I guess I'll just have to share my contacts with you, then. We can't have you going home empty-handed," he laughed before rummaging in the wardrobe and producing a small notebook. "You're welcome to this, Kel. Please don't lose it."

How thoughtful. The booklet contained notes on flea markets and antique shops within a day's travel from Sendai. He cautioned none of them boasted English lettering but I wasn't fussed. I'd simply compare his Kanji to those posted outside the shops. That method hadn't failed me yet.

I set out early the next morning. It was reassuring to discover that Pierre's sources were vastly different from the elegant Hong Kong "Nail Tapping" enterprise. The majority were tiny, poorly lit, and crammed to the ceiling, oozing magical possibilities. They all smelled the same, too; like the airless attic of a committed hoarder.

I missed Francine immediately. I pictured her sashaying in, boldly announcing, "We are buyers from Vancouver, Canada, hoping to purchase many wondrous things."

I unfortunately lacked that chutzpah. When I waved politely at the man sitting toward the back, he leapt up and walked toward me. My introverted side roared to life.

"I am just looking, thank you," I muttered before remembering to bow as I'd seen Pierre do. He backed away. Gratified, I nodded and slowly circled the shop. He sold only antique maps. Not for me. I waved goodbye and headed for the exit. However, the shopkeeper didn't get it. He hustled over again.

"You have lovely maps. However, I am not in need of one. Thank you. Have a good day," I flapped my fingers in farewell. The fellow, now looking more than a little annoyed, reluctantly shuffled closer. I scuttled out quickly.

A similar situation happened again in the antique armament shop and also at the bookshop. Why didn't Pierre didn't warn me about this intense merchant behavior? Then it hit me. Sweet mother of God. The fault was *mine*. They were reacting to my innocent hand-cupping. I was waving goodbye like a child would, as if I was squeezing a ball in my hand. In Canada that could pass as both a greeting and a farewell. But in Japan, it meant, "come here." The poor merchants. I'd been visually reeling them in and then verbally casting them away. On repeat. No wonder folks were confused and upset.

That sorted, I steeled myself to enter a fourth shop. This one looked more promising. It hosted not only an eclectic array of furniture, but also bundles of rolled-up scrolls. Bingo. Several scrolls could easily fit in a suitcase. Going through the piles would take time, but never mind. It would take as long as it took.

With my hands planted firmly at my sides, I bowed to the shopkeeper and hunkered down. The fact that many edges were torn or watermarked didn't dissuade me. My dear art professor of a mother had trained me well. I could do this. What mattered was the condition of the actual artwork. We could always chop off the tattered borders and frame the remainder.

Being familiar with our customers' wish lists helped tremendously. I easily recalled Beth and Susan's fondness for roosters, Doris's preference for blue iris and Mrs. Park's partiality toward mice. With those fronts soon covered, I focused on scrolls that spoke to me.

I then moved on to textiles. The numbers on offer were overwhelming. Francine could have opened a second shop had I the funds and ability to transport them all home. I homed in on two options, anticipating my mother's reaction to the red and gold wedding obis ("stunning table runners, Kel") and the charming children's kimonos ("perfect as wall hangings").

Pierre was most impressed. By the end of the second day, he insisted on lending me a large suitcase for the trip home. I'd unearthed some magnificent antique hand mirrors that afternoon. Made of bronze, the sturdy narrow handles supported flat, circular tops ranging in size from saucers to salad plates. The fronts were polished to reflect the handler's image and the backs were carved, mostly with decorative trees or flowers. Always too expensive in Portland and Honolulu, here they were very reasonable. I selected the perfect one for Evelyn and after much deliberation, bought two other beauts. It broke my heart to reject a pair of exquisite lacquer dressing table boxes equipped with tiny drawers and folded mirrors, but they were just too large to cart home.

There was no way I could pass up the gorgeous, circular hibachi made of burnished paulownia wood, however. The size of a tiny ottoman, it had Julia's name all over it. I knew she would love it. If I couldn't jam it into the bottom of a suitcase, stuffed full of rolled up clothing, it would dazzle as my aircraft carry-on.

I was growing painfully smug and it just took one sharp-eyed taxi driver to straighten me out. When the fare came to the equivalent of $8, I loftily inferred that he was to "keep the change." The fellow snatched the bills from my fingers and zoomed off with the passenger door still flapping. Of course he did. I'd blessed him with a $100 tip.

Once Pierre stopped laughing, he had the perfect solution for the excessive overpayment.

"I'll buy that hibachi for double what you paid for it, Kelly. It's brilliant."

"Sorry, Pierre. Flight attendant Julia gets first refusal."

My roommate frowned and studied me, his head cocked to the side.

"Mon dieu, mon amie. You've come a long way. A few years ago, you'd have let me have it at cost."

I smiled and shook my head. "No, back then I wouldn't have had the smarts to buy it in the first place."

I rounded off the week by accepting an invitation to dinner with the Kameis. Pierre's astonishment was gratifying. He assured me that it was considered a great honor to be asked to go to someone's home and not a restaurant.

When we arrived at their modest wood-framed house on the quiet, narrow street, Mr. Kamei's similarity to Mr. Rogers was even more acute. He was wearing a pale yellow cardigan and a pair of crisp gray slacks. His charming wife immediately apologized for her "poor English" and welcomed us warmly. Their eldest son, who was in his late teens and taller than his parents, zipped in for a quick introduction before excusing himself to finish his homework. His younger brother would join us later.

It soon felt as if we'd been friends for years. Their decor, while modern, reflected a home rather than a showroom. Family photos were scattered everywhere and the furniture was designed with an eye for comfort. Mrs. Kamei's English was nearly as proficient as her husband's. After a pleasant half-hour of small talk, she invited me into the kitchen. The amount of food she'd prepared was staggering. Several pots were boiling on the stove, and the counters were already covered with beautifully prepared treats.

We sat down at a table laden with platters of fish, chicken, rice, noodles and vegetable greens. Our hosts explained the symbolism of the different items and, when pressed, generously described how each was prepared. As we tucked into the meal, the conversation flowed easily. After a lively discussion about the highlights of their many North American holidays, the Kameis politely turned to Pierre. They were curious about his teaching position and whether he was enjoying living in Japan. He assured them it was all he thought it would be, and more.

"And you, Kelly," Mrs. Kamei smiled. "My husband says you are here to buy antiques. Why? Most people here don't wish to keep old things. It is fascinating that you do."

The genuine interest had me sharing more family history than usual. Pierre added his own tidbits, helping the Kameis understand how my mother's deep interest in their culture led me here.

With her husband now insisting he would look after the washing up, she invited us into her studio. The woman was a gifted *sumi-e* (black ink painting) artist. She created the most beautiful illustrations using handmade paper or *washi*. Sensing our interest, she gave us a quick lesson in the art of calligraphy. The speed at which her brush flew over the paper was mind boggling.

While Pierre acknowledged the huge effort to make us feel truly welcome, it wasn't until much later that we realized the Kameis didn't ask one question concerning our relationship.

CHAPTER 45

You Just Never Know

T he three weeks in Japan flew by. I arrived back in Vancouver on January 27th, 1988, and while I was excited to share my secret financing plan with my boss, it would have to wait. I'd been up for 36 hours and couldn't string two words together.

Francine had news, too. When I reported for work, she insisted we admire FROG's window display. The effect could best be described as, "less is more." There was one focal point: a large *katana-dansu* (sword chest) blessed with a gleaming keyaki wood front. Chunky lapis lazuli necklaces, colorful Thai silk shawls and ropes of Tibetan prayer beads spilled from the four open drawers. I loved it.

"It's very different from our usual efforts! Did you get help, Francine?"

My mother pranced Tigger-like beside me on the sidewalk.

"Yes! Dave helped. He used to be a window dresser for Woodward's!"

Our Boxing Day host had done the Woodward's windows? The recently defunct department store chain, a British Columbian fixture for a century, was famous for its legendary window displays. No wonder this current FROG effort was so strong.

"How'd you two get along?" I prodded.

"Just fine, thank you," she sniffed.

Taking note of my smirk, she admitted, "Okay, Dave did fuss rather excessively but we parted as friends. Good friends. The man cheerfully worked a solid three hours on just two cups of coffee. Come on, let's go inside and warm up. I'm dying to hear about your trip."

I carefully laid out the scrolls, hibachi, mirrors and textiles. As was typical of my mother, she swooned over the items, without asking the prices of any.

"You are clever. Well done, Kel."

"Do you think we can make a profit, Mom?"

"There's only one way to find out. Get on the blower and bring in the troops."

Beth and Susan were the first to respond. I tried to appear nonchalant while they studied the rooster scroll.

"Wow. You did well, Kelly. We'll take it, right, Beth?"

Her partner nodded with delight. Julia's reaction to the hibachi was also positive.

"The wood grain is spectacular. Are you sure you don't want to keep it for yourself, Kelly?" she asked.

"Well, I am tempted," I teased.

She snatched it from my hands.

"Sorry, it's mine. But I'll happily give you visitation rights."

Initially flummoxed by the "novel concept" of a personal shopper, Mrs. Park recovered quickly. She snapped up the scampering mice scroll and requested first refusal rights on the iris one should Doris not want it.

My confidence was off the charts when Doris rolled in, until she came closer. The woman looked very upset. Something was seriously wrong.

Francine noticed it too.

"What good timing, Doris. I'm gasping for tea."

When they returned over an hour later, I discreetly waggled the scroll at Francine, and received the quickest of nods in return. I shoved it into one of our bags along with the invoice and withdrew into the office to afford them more privacy.

"You won't believe it, Kel," a subdued Francine called out the second Doris left.

"Is she ill, Mom?"

"No. Ben and she are divorced! They finalized it two months ago. She's gone back to her maiden name."

A colorful highlight reel of the past five years flashed before my eyes. The exuberant Doris skipping in, ecstatic over the discovery of the ancestor portraits, Ben's "near death experience" in the pool at the farm, his petulant negotiations over the wedding baskets, the births of their first child, their second and finally their third.

My heart ached for them all.

"How sad, Mom."

"It is, Kel. She has custody of the kids and is considering a move. But who knows? It's all still pretty fresh. I never could have guessed, could you?"

No.

As for my Japanese purchases? I managed to make more money for FROG than Francine had doled out for my trip. Not bad for someone who originally didn't know an obi from a California roll.

CHAPTER 46

Running on Full

Carly was dropping broad hints about an impending change in her relationship status with John by the end of February. By March, she admitted they were now just friends. When she accepted his sister's invitation to John's surprise 30th birthday party, we arranged to go together. I struggled with the perfect outfit and finally settled on the infamous over-sized, fiery orange sweater emboldened with the giant Picasso-like beaded profile. It was fun and current.

I immediately regretted it, just as I had with the Yamamotos. Carly looked elegant and well put-together in her classic pale blue cardigan and black pencil skirt. However, with no time to go home and change, I wrenched the car into reverse and lurched toward the exit of the parking lot. A most alarming thump suddenly sounded directly underneath the vehicle. I cut the engine.

"No worries, Carly, I'll just hop out for a wee look. I'm sure it's nothing dire."

Christ! I'd marooned the car smack on top of a concrete block. Carly's look of utter disbelief was understandable, especially considering that there was only one such block in the entire parking lot. She scowled at her watch.

"If you'd be good enough to steady the steering wheel, I'll shove us off," I calmly instructed in my best Emma Thompson impression.

I planted my feet and pushed with everything I had. The car rocked but refused to budge. We needed a tow truck.

Our savior arrived within fifteen minutes. He hopped out of the shiny white truck and slowly circled my car. When I sheepishly shrugged, the fellow grinned, attached a lead and yanked us back onto solid ground.

"It happens more often than you'd think, Ma'am," he kindly said, handing me back my credit card. "I'll wait while you fire her up. Hopefully you've not damaged the undercarriage."

All three of us hooted with delight as the car roared to life.

Our luck continued to hold. The birthday boy was also running late. We joined the 30 other guests in his parents' darkened living room as John's car pulled into the driveway.

Kudos to his sister. John was truly surprised. She shoved a drink into his hand and he cheerfully worked his way through the crowd, chatting at length with each of his guests. It was at least 45 minutes and two rum and Cokes later before he got to me.

"What a great sweater, Kelly. It's good to see you. Can I offer you a quick tour? There's something I want to show you."

He had me at "great sweater."

When I made note of the celadon plate on the mantelpiece, John inquired about other FROG potentials. After discerning that the interest was genuine, I pointed out the Korean wedding basket and the Chinese porcelain peach.

"Okay, my turn. Check out the third shelf," John teased, pointing to the china cabinet in a corner of the living room.

Our stone pig. It was just as I remembered: brown, stocky and blessed with perky ears and a wrinkled nose.

"Mom's looking after it for me until I'm settled in my new place," John explained, referring to the condo he'd purchased and was now renovating with his father.

His sister quietly intervened. It was cake time.

I mingled happily with the other guests for the rest of the night. Everyone was eager to share their story of how they knew the birthday boy. As expected, none could top our unique porcine tale.

When John invited me to join him in the fourth annual 10K Vancouver Sun Run several weeks later, I reluctantly accepted. Having not laced up my running shoes in weeks, I dreaded the challenging hills. I knew the route well. Both of my marathon training groups had treated the Sun Runs as warmups on lengthy training days. Yet, here we were, just a year later, and I was fretting over not being able to complete the six miles.

After he maintained an easy banter throughout, I realized it was time to let John fly. At my suggestion, he kicked into another gear and flew up the Burrard Street bridge on the home stretch. When I finally gasped across the finish line, he tossed me a banana, and nodding toward the lengthy lines at the crowded post-run water and fruit stations, offered to whip us up a restorative brunch.

The afternoon passed pleasantly. The conversation flowed and I managed to avoid making an ass of myself, unlike my shameful performance at the symphony with Allan.

CHAPTER 47

Papa Gus Versus Godfrey

John and I were a couple by June of '88. He had met all of the key folks in my life, but one. My father. That was on me. I would have happily welcomed a complicated root canal procedure over that.

While the majority of the FROG customers either met handyman "Fred" or Francine's genial husband Geoff, it was different with my friends. They met the funny, humble and insightful Godfrey. However, toss in the boyfriend concept and Godfrey morphed into Gus Portokalos, Toula's father in the classic film *My Big Fat Greek Wedding*. My personal Papa Gus scrutinized dates with the intensity of an overly suspicious border guard. Once he formed an opinion, it was impossible to change his mind.

A particularly visceral memory still haunts me. The plans were solid. A quick introduction over drinks at the folks', followed by dinner at *The Cannery Seafood Restaurant,* a family favorite. However, my date and I arrived late. So much for the drinks. My parents were already hunkered down in their car with the engine running, as if fleeing a bank heist. All because of a mere ten-minute oversight. I was mortified. I caught Francine's apologetic "I know, I'm sorry," but my date didn't. The unsuspecting soul bounded over with all the enthusiasm of a toddler. Papa Gus snaked his fingers through a minutely lowered window and offered up a chilly fingertip shake. Message received. We were in for one hell of an evening.

There was no way I'd expose Mrs. McKenzie's son to that. Nope, these two special guys would meet only after I'd hatched a thoroughly thought-out plan, something John didn't quite understand at first. After patiently listening to my lengthy dissertation, he flashed me a reassuring smile.

"You needn't worry, Kel. I'm good with parents."

Fair enough. But Papa Gus was on a *whole* other level. I touched on the particulars of the "fingertip shake" story and was mollified by John's appropriate level of shock.

"Okay, I vote that we nix the eating out concept, Kel. We need a casual meet-and-greet scenario at somewhere neutral. I'm there, he's there and we bump into each other."

I liked it and only added one codicil. The intro must happen before Godfrey got wise to our relationship or we'd open ourselves up to a major Papa Gus flareup.

We got lucky. With two large shipments arriving from Portland and Honolulu a week later, Francine and I organized another FROG evening soiree complete with a harpist and the usual booze and appies. Our regular caterers were booked but when John managed to engage his friends, who moonlighted for a local company, as replacements, we extended an invitation to him, as "a thank you." Perfect. The stage was set for Dad and John to finally meet.

Francine was also nervous. As we approached the opening time, John's friend Mary pointed out my mother's fondness for messing with their appetizer platters. Poor Francine. These soirees were always a crap shoot. So much was out of our control. We never knew how many customers would show up or how much would sell. Tonight was especially dicey with a great deal of money invested in the two inventory shipments.

"I'd no idea the harp would be so big, did you, Kel?" Francine hissed as I steered her away from the platters. No. It was huge. We struggled for ten minutes before managing to wedge the harpist and her instrument in between the platform stairs and a slender life-size *Quan Yin* statue. With just enough elbow room to efficiently pluck the strings, God help her if she had an urgent need to use the bathroom.

Francine and I were soon busier than a Harrods' Boxing Day sale. Our regulars had learned it was best to arrive early before all the "good pieces" got sold. However, once John arrived, looking very smart in his navy blazer and gray flannels, time stopped. My endorphins shot into overdrive and I dashed to the bathroom to hold a damp cloth to my fiery cheeks.

I emerged to find Godfrey alone in a corner, happily tucking into a plate of appetizers. I dodged the harpist to flag down John; a flashing neon arrow would have been more subtle. He smothered a grin and after kibitzing a bit with Mary and grabbing a white wine from her husband David, casually sauntered over to inspect a rather divine two-piece keyaki wood *isho-dansu* (clothing chest) that just happened to be next to Godfrey.

The two men exchanged polite smiles and a handshake. I felt positively legless. It was a proper handshake complete with full finger and palm involvement. John eased into a series of questions regarding the tansu. Dad clearly appreciated the genuine interest. He began opening various drawers and pointing out the elegant locks and handles. When the pair dropped onto the floor to inspect the craftsman's signature inked in kanji on the underside of the bottom drawer, that was it. I knew. John had met Godfrey. I found it difficult to concentrate on anything else. My heart pinched as Dad ushered his protege over to meet Beth and Susan. The flurry of introductions were orchestrated without a hint of Papa Gus stiffness. As the jolly foursome edged closer, I caught fragments of the conversation.

"My mom has mentioned something called a 'floating panel,' Geoff. I don't really understand how it works. Can you show me some examples?" John asked easily.

Godfrey led the troops over to an elegant antique Chinese wooden altar table. He pointed out the clever fashioning of the top that allowed for both expansion and shrinkage without any of the usual cracks or fissures.

"Your father's enjoying himself eh, Kel? I'm so glad. He usually finds these parties tiresome," Francine whispered, before sailing off into the crowd to greet some new arrivals. I followed suit, fully confident that John had things well in hand.

When the harpist was safely extracted and the friendly caterers dispatched, it was just after 10:30. The evening had gone well; the sales slips were piled almost an inch thick. I was sorting through the checks when Francine wearily announced, "Kel, leave it. We'll deal with them tomorrow."

John shot me a quick query and I nodded.

"You and Geoff go home, Frankie," he suggested. "I'll stay and help Kelly tidy and close up. Don't worry, I'll make sure she gets to her car safely."

My heart melted as Godfrey slowly grinned and slapped John on the back. "Good man. I hope we see more of you."

CHAPTER 48

Alert the Paparazzi

F rancine was about to land the mother lode of a newsworthy scoop. Gossip we couldn't and wouldn't share. Not with anyone.

Fortunately, we were used to keeping secrets.

Vancouver was known as Canada's "Hollywood North" by the late '80s. TV and movie set decorators were always on the hunt for quality items with which to dress their sets. We welcomed their business. They happily paid our competitive rental fees and there was never any silliness over pieces damaged during filming. They simply bought them outright.

Cannell Studios was an early player. They often rented contemporary and antique items for the popular TV series *21 Jump Street*, starring a youthful Johnny Depp. While we never set eyes on Mr. Depp, we did welcome several celebrities to FROG. Some well-known, others not so much. Regardless of their popularity, we always kept their visits on the down-low, just as we did with everyone. It wasn't difficult. Mrs.Tungsten's bride's jar saga still stung.

My first experience with a local celebrity was in the 10th Avenue shop. When the couple meandered in one Saturday afternoon, there was something oddly familiar about the guy's angular jaw and mop of floppy gray hair. However, proper identification would have to wait as his wife wanted a closer look at the Buddha in the window.

At just over sixteen inches high and covered in 24 karat gold, the nineteenth century Burmese seated bronze Buddha was a prime example of the Mandalay style, with folded drapery, a sweet, peaceful face and a large mound of tight curly hair that could be mistaken for a bun. I'd recently learned that the hair actually covered the *ushnisha*, Buddha's bump of enlightened knowledge.

I scampered onto the window platform while Francine prepared the groundwork.

"Isn't he magnificent? I found him languishing in a tiny antique shop in Honolulu." FROG's founder ran her fingers through her hair, sighing. "It's an honor to live with him until he finds his proper home."

As I lowered the cumbersome bulk onto a nearby altar table, mindful of my fingers, the couple's reactions were markedly disparate. She eagerly encircled the figure like a predatory cat, while Mystery Man melted into the wall by the door. It was obvious that he didn't wish to engage. His niggling familiarity became a compulsion.

"Are you practicing Buddhists?" I blurted.

It was as if I'd skewered him with the meat fork. I blushed deeply. What an intrusive question. Yet I couldn't stop myself. Who *was* he? Random memories flitted about my brain like the viscous globs in a lava lamp, before a single strand finally peeled away and rocketed to the surface.

"Trash!"

Francine's face confirmed the worst. I'd not only spoken out loud, but I'd done so in a monosyllabic outburst likely overheard by the tellers at the bank across the street.

"You're the *trash* man!" I gabbled, scrambling to make things right.

"Kelly. Please!"

Francine's fury could have blistered tempered glass. Was the Buddha sale slipping away?

"You did a series of garbage bag commercials, didn't you?" I asked, my voice now bordering on hysteria. "And I think ... also one for some over-the-counter sleep meds?"

Everything changed in that moment. Acknowledging that he was indeed "trash man" and "insomnia patient," the actor became chatty and charming. As Francine and the couple began to cheerfully hammer out mutually agreeable sales terms, I turned to the Buddha and offered up silent thanks for the activation of my personal bump of knowledge. It couldn't have been more timely.

As the actor staggered out with their bubble-wrapped treasure, Francine shook her head, frowning.

"Things could have ended *so* very differently. You've got to rein yourself in, Kelly."

After a good half-hour of deliberate separation, we slowly found our way back to each other and began to hammer out a more professional response. Going forward, unless a celebrity identified themself, we'd take their modesty as a sign that they chose to fly under the radar.

The first recipient of this strategy? The late Cliff Robertson. I recognized the Oscar-winning actor the second he entered the Granville Street location. However, Francine did not. She greeted the deeply tanned, ruggedly handsome actor with a pleasantly preoccupied, "Please, sing out if we can answer any questions," and withdrew.

Seriously? He was one of her favorite actors.

"Cliff. *Star 80.* Hefner." I whispered, subtly jerking my head in his direction. Francine frowned.

"*PT 109, PT 109.*" I hissed, my lips now inches from her ear. She glared at me in confusion.

"Petey, who? Whatever are you on about?"

Dear Lord.

"War movie. JFK. Sinking boat." I spat, staccato-like.

The actor inched toward the door. FROG wasn't for him. Francine's head suddenly snapped up in recognition. The actor graced us with a heartfelt, "Thanks, ladies" and slipped out. Our subsequent fan-girl squeals followed him down the block.

Francine beamed when the actor who played Barney Miller on the popular TV show of the same name, strolled into FROG a few months later. Of course, she recognized him. Who wouldn't? He played Captain Miller for some 170 episodes over eight seasons. We were gutted when the show shut down in 1982.

Francine greeted him and his partner with the appropriate amount of grace. While the actor held back (just as Barney would have), the gorgeous redhead smiled warmly.

"Our hotel concierge recommended your store. My husband and I are looking for quirky table bases."

"How delightful. We have several that might fill the bill. Let me show you."

Francine swept them over to our ever-popular trio of contemporary Thai bronze penguins. I'd just finished polishing the circular charcoal-gray glass top. The life-size seabird ensemble looked its very best.

"They're fun. Do you like them, Frances?" the actor asked.

"You're a Frances? Me, too!" Francine squealed. "Are you ever called Frankie?"

How fortuitous. With the two women now giggling over the various nicknames they'd received over the years, I suddenly had the actor all to myself. My knees nearly gave out as Mr. Linden rolled his eyes and winked.

"We'll leave them to it, shall we? Can you show me the other options?"

With my head buzzing, I willed myself to act professional. However, my fair complexion let me down. It flushed fuchsia, not dissimilar to the color of youthful swiss chard stems. Damn. Unable to form a cogent sentence, I bent forward almost to the floor, and waved him toward the back of the shop. He kindly didn't comment.

We lurched to a halt next to the bowed backs of a pair of life-size, scantily dressed, kneeling wooden boys. I giggled when he rubbed his hands over his face and began to laugh.

"Those would sure stir up some interesting conversations. Have you anything else?"

His wife called out, "Hal, come and check out this Chinese antique picnic basket. I think it'd be perfect as a wedding present for Don."

My hopes for a cozy one-on-one sales consultation evaporated, however all was not lost. The couple charmed us for the next half hour as they carefully considered each of the tablebase options. When it came time for our new friends to leave, Francine looked as sad as I felt. I volunteered to write up the sales slip while she phoned for a cab.

"No need to tell me your name," I blathered, as Mr. Linden fished in his wallet for a credit card. The revelation seemed to both surprise and humor him. He raised an eyebrow and flashed me a respectful smile, just as I'd seen Barney do a dozen times over.

When their taxi pulled into the traffic, Francine turned to me with a puzzled smile.

"Was it just me, Kel, or did Mr. Linden seem kind of familiar to you?"

Fade to black …

However, when it came to the gentleman who would share the momentous scoop, the boss recognized him immediately. I hadn't a clue.

"Welcome to my shop, Mr. Pocklington," Francine beamed, blatantly ignoring our celebrity game plan. "We've met before. The first time was a few years ago at the Edmonton antique fair!"

The multimillionaire, then-owner of the Edmonton Oilers professional ice hockey team, didn't remember, but was flattered that she did. The two were soon chatting comfortably and I slipped out to the bank. By the time I got back, he'd completed a hefty purchase. Francine insisted that I help him out to his car. Thanks, Mom. He'd opted for two of the bulkiest and most fragile pieces in the shop. However, one didn't embarrass the boss by refusing. I lugged my charge outside and up the sidewalk to his roomy rental vehicle.

Unfortunately he returned just moments later, looking frazzled. He'd locked his keys in the car and required a wire hanger.

"My daughter can help." Francine called out as he dashed for the door. "Kelly's quite experienced in that department."

My chest swelled with pride. I'd get that door unlocked in a jiff.

The businessman pointed to the keys dangling from the ignition. Before I could ask for the hanger, he fashioned the hook into a narrow loop and carefully slipped it under the window's rubber lining.

The man had skill. I held my breath as he slipped it over the door lock and, ever so slowly, tugged up the nub. Boom. Peter Pocklington was back in business. He pocketed the keys, locked the door and insisted on returning the hanger to Francine personally.

"As my special thanks to you, Frankie, I'll share a certain tidbit that is about to rock the sporting world. Don't share it with anyone before it breaks."

We solemnly swore we wouldn't.

"Wayne Gretzky has been traded to the Los Angeles Kings."

No! That couldn't be true. The great Wayne Gretzky had led the Edmonton Oilers to four Stanley Cups in five years. He was *our* guy. He *couldn't* be heading to an American team. Wow. The news would rock Canada. What a scoop.

And Francine and I couldn't tell a soul.

Thankfully, we only had to hold on for one night. Gretzky's trade was announced the next day – August 9, 1988.

I do sometimes wonder if I dreamed we were privy to this momentous news a day before the rest of the world. But her diary always confirms it. We certainly were.

CHAPTER 49

Wedded Miss

W e called Ed first when someone dropped off a small multi-drawer *kiri* or paulownia wood tansu for us to sell on consignment. He'd been looking for a side table for months. However, when he gave it just a cursory glance, I knew something was up.

"Do you remember Paula, Kelly? You met her at the Monster Trucks night."

No, I didn't. It was well over a year ago now.

"Tall? Redhead?"

Still nothing.

"Well, she's getting married. Several folks from work are going and I'd love it if you'd come with me, Kelly. However, I understand if you can't. It's on a Saturday afternoon."

That was my out.

"I'm so sorry, Ed. I'm going to have to decline. It'd be different if it was in the evening, but …"

"Nonsense, Kel. Of course, you can go. I'm happy to hold the fort on my own. What's the date, Ed? I'll put it in the day book," the hovering Francine declared.

His face flushed with joy as my mother carefully jotted down the details.

"How lovely that we've another chance to help him out, Kelly. He's such a dear," Francine murmured as he carted the chest out to his car.

Yes, Ed was a dear. However, the concept of play-acting as his girlfriend was no less stressful than before. Of course, my concerns about everyone discovering I was a sham girlfriend were minor compared to his reality, but the situation was still tricky.

I felt even worse once I realized the wedding was on the very Saturday I was invited to spend the night at the McKenzie's cabin on the Sunshine Coast. I was supposed to go directly to the ferry after work and John would meet me on the other side.

Of course, Francine's commitment to Ed was as irrevocable as mine was to John. She insisted I could do both.

"Kel, the backyard wedding is at 1:00 with the reception right after. You're only an hour from home. If you leave by 3:45, you'll have time to get changed at home before catching the 6 p.m. boat out of the Horseshoe Bay terminal. Easy."

"I sure hope so, Mom. The next ferry isn't for two hours. That'd get me into the terminal at 8:45. John and I wouldn't be sitting down to eat until 9:30 if I catch the later one."

When I stressed the importance of catching the 6:00 ferry to Ed, he assured me it was doable. John wasn't convinced, but nevermind. His skepticism only made me more determined.

The weather on the nuptial day was iconically autumnal: sunny, breezy and crisp. As I followed Ed down the crowded row on the bride's side of the grassy aisle, I could hear his colleagues whispering about what a cute couple we made. A few even winked and waved.

The bride was late. When Paula and her father graced us with their presence at 1:30, Ed nudged me gently.

"Remember her now, Kelly?" he twinkled.

Not a jot.

The ceremony went off without another hitch. Once the I-do's were uttered, we had a good hour-and-a-half window. Plenty of time. As we joined the lineup to congratulate the newly married couple, Bev and Milly and a handful of his colleagues joined us.

"I do love a garden wedding. Would you get married outside, Kelly?" Milly asked after we shuffled past the last of the wedding party and headed to the bar.

"Ha. She'd have to book acreage! Most of their customers would be clamoring to attend," Ed smoothly deflected.

The two women exchanged knowing looks and I smothered a smile. They really had no idea.

My main concern now was ensuring I didn't impale my heels into the pristine turf.

"Aerating the lawn, are we? I could use you at our place," Ed teased, passing me a glass of Sauvignon Blanc large enough to bathe in. He really was great fun.

"Let's grab some food before we go," I suggested, hooking my arm in his. We crunched onto the gravel path in search of the food tent.

"Go? You can't go yet! Things are just getting underway," Bev protested. She called out to her husband, "Murray, talk some sense into this man."

"She's right, Ed. Come on. Ralph wants to chat." Murray winked, tapping the fistful of cigars poking out of his breast pocket.

Ed leaned in to hiss, "It's a union bigwig, I need to have a quick word. I won't be long."

I was about to make some wisecrack about private confabs

between the Godfather and his consigliere when Bev piped up with yet another inanity.

"How sweet of Ed to explain why he was leaving. My husband tends to just disappear." She elbowed her colleague. "Things certainly change once the ring's on the finger, eh, Milly?"

I dug deep and prattled off a slew of random questions concerning Paula the bride, her groom and their honeymoon plans. The resulting conviviality attracted the attention of others, and the conversation mercifully skated far away from all-things-Ed-and-Kelly.

When the men finally reappeared, some wag suggested the two of us join the gang for dinner at a local restaurant. I panicked and dug my nails painfully into Ed's hand.

"We'd love to join you, but Kelly's got a prior engagement with a 6 o'clock ferry. Her mother would kill me if she didn't make it."

"Oh, too bad. But you're right. It's best to keep on good terms with the future in-laws, Ed," Bev reluctantly agreed.

We finally managed to escape at 4:00.

Despite Ed's best efforts, I was late. The ferry was just leaving the slip as I dashed toward the ticket booth. I now had two hours to kill before the next boat, a reality I dreaded telling John. It took me several moments to compose myself, and by the time I made it to the waiting room there was no line for the pay phone. I dialed his number slowly.

"You missed the ferry? *How?* Dinner's all ready. I was just about to leave to get you, Kelly," John snapped in frustration. "Who is this guy again?"

The stress of the afternoon and John's understandable disappointment were too much. I gently hung up. It was our first argument, albeit a tad one-sided.

John's sky blue Datsun 510 was idling in the passenger pickup line when I trudged off the ferry almost three hours later. He stepped out with a look of deep chagrin and handed me a cloth-covered bowl.

"A peace offering, Kel."

I drew back the cotton tea towel and nearly burst into tears at the sight of two mouthwatering cheese scones.

"They're fresh out of the oven. You must be starving," John smiled as he started the car.

As my teeth sunk into the cheesy deliciousness, it hit me. This was right. It felt real and good and honest. Ed would have to do without me from now on. Today marked my last performance as his girlfriend.

CHAPTER 50

Can You Say, "Send In the Repairman?"

Francine and I had just survived the first full day of our two-week buying trip in the fall of '88, only to discover our Hong Kong hotel room's cooling system was on the fritz.

"Christ. I'm dripping. Can you do anything with the AC, Kel?" Francine asked before collapsing onto her bed.

How about turning it on? There's a concept. I twirled the air conditioner knob and flounced into the bathroom. There was nothing like jet lag and being thrown together twenty-four/seven to mess with my patience.

In dire need of some me-time, I filled the tub and took full advantage of the hotel's extensive toiletry offerings. I emerged twenty minutes later to find a florid Francine perched on the edge of her bed, barking into the phone. The room was even hotter than before.

"Yes, wonky. *W-O-N-K-Y.*" My mother flashed me a quick eye roll. "*Not working.* Yes, that's right. *No* air conditioner. Too much heat. Thank you and do hurry. We're dripping up here!"

Dearly regretting my lingering soak, I was now fully on board with her sense of urgency.

"We won't sleep a wink until it's fixed, Kel," my mother predicted, ditching her duvet and climbing on top of the sheets. "Turn down the TV, please. We need to hear them knock."

Seriously? She already had the volume so low, the network news was barely discernible. But nevermind. She could lip read. I pressed mute and cracked open my pulpy paperback. A mere ten minutes later, the familiar repetitive notes of "fff ... fff ... fff," commenced. Francine had officially entered stage one of her snoring pattern: Gentle Puffs.

I soon made out a soft tapping. As I spied the youthful custodian in a pair of crisp overalls and a white T-shirt through the privacy peep hole, I cracked open the door. Francine couldn't fault his promptness.

I greeted him with a cautionary finger plastered to my lips and he nodded, slowly easing a metal step-ladder into the room. Francine stirred as he propped it open at the foot of her bed but rather than fully awaken, she advanced to stage two: Squeegeeing. With her snores now replicating the sound of rubber blades being dragged across a barely wet pane of glass, the fellow scrambled up the ladder, dislodged the ceiling panel and disappeared. The room temperature was now borderline satanic.

"I see the problem." The repairman whispered, popping his head out. "I can do a temporary fix but it'll make a little bit of noise," he warned.

I flashed him a thumbs up.

I soon found the combination of Francine's squeaks and the pounding of metal on metal surprisingly mellifluous. Either that or I was in the early phases of heatstroke.

"Okay, I'm just about done," he called out fifteen minutes later. Francine bolted upright, her silver hair ballooning out wildly like a dandelion gone to seed.

"*Who's just about done?*" she shrieked.

She peered up at the pair of legs now stiffly dangling from the ceiling and hollered, "Don't you *dare* lay a hand on my daughter!"

"Mom. Stop! I'm right here! He's the *air-conditioning guy*," I hissed, horrified.

She rose up onto her knees and punched a fist skyward.

"Don't you *dare* touch her!" She spat, saliva flying.

The poor fellow vanished into the ceiling. I heard a definitive tap, and the maligned maintenance man suddenly slid onto the floor. My slew of apologies had little effect. He folded up his ladder and fled. Francine flopped backwards onto her bed and resumed the gentle puffs.

The room temperature dropped considerably but I found it impossible to sleep. I finally dropped off around 3:00.

Of course, Francine woke early, pleasantly refreshed.

"Well, it certainly is cooler, Kel. What a relief the temperature sorted itself out."

I brought her up to speed over a delicious breakfast of French toast. She probably still suspects me of embellishment.

Today's itinerary included a visit to a source we discovered in January. The tiny antique shop was conveniently situated near Stanley Market on Hong Kong Island. Our previous purchases of their cinnabar lacquer picnic boxes, bamboo bird cages, blue and white porcelain hat stands and ceramic pillows, bowls and stools, had sold particularly well and we were eager to restock.

The owner had an unfortunate habit of nattering on about her daughter's achievements, and we decided it would be best to divide and conquer this time. One of us would scout out the inventory while the other absorbed the litany of daughter Diana's latest accomplishments. We'd then switch places.

As before, we were the only customers. Francine gently reminded the woman that we were "the mother-and-daughter team from Vancouver, Canada."

"Of course. How nice that you have returned. And so soon." Her joyous face suddenly collapsed. "Unfortunately, my daughter Diana is in school today. Did you meet her last time?"

"No, we've yet to have that pleasure," Francine admitted.

"Oh, that's too bad. She's 12 now. Her teacher has tasked her with a fascinating science project involving water and electrolysis ..."

As mater launched into the finer details of her daughter's project, I eased away to slowly circle the room. Unfortunately, the items on hand were disappointing and I quickly swapped places with Francine, just in time to learn that Diana had received top marks in the latest spelling test. My boss's perusal was even quicker than my own and, after the briefest confab, we settled on a few picnic baskets and one or two blue and white pieces, all of which we could carry home.

The merchant began to wrap our purchases and I popped into the washroom. It put ours to shame; we truly needed to up our game. The flocked wallpaper, thick towels, and the antique basket stocked with samples of mouthwash and packages of Q-tips were impressive. There was only one jarring note: the hefty green plastic beaker plunked on top of the toilet tank.

When the toilet refused to flush, I pressed down firmly on the plastic handle. There was no improvement. I jiggled the handle up and down, only to have a sizable chunk snap off. Panicking, I pinched the remaining nubbin with my fingertips and tried again. Thankfully it flushed. But I dreaded leaving the bathroom. With Diana's mother already upset at our paltry purchases, I could only imagine how this unfortunate predicament would affect our relationship.

"Hurry up, Kel! I have to go!"

Francine pushed past me before I could enlighten her of the distressing development.

"Kelly, come and see Diana's latest school picture! Your mother agrees she's amongst the prettiest in the class."

The photo of the innocent girl in her school uniform was arresting. My tongue clamped onto the roof of my mouth as I realized Perfect Daughter would never be in this situation. Ever. I couldn't bring myself to confess. My guilt worsened as Francine suddenly emerged from the bathroom and made for the door, calling out a pert goodbye. We booked it for the anonymity of Stanley Market, stopping only when we were deep in the thick of it.

"I don't think we can ever go back, Kelly, " Francine mumbled.

"Oh God. I'm so sorry, Mom," I replied, my voice catching.

Francine bowed her head.

"I've done a dreadful thing," she moaned, now barely above a whisper.

I struggled to catch up.

"When the toilet wouldn't flush, I remembered Dad's advice to try adding water. There was this plastic jug on top of the tank and I hurled the entire contents down the toilet. Oh Lord." She looked at me with haunted eyes. "I think I might have just chucked out Diana's science project!" As Francine paused to let that possibility percolate, my fingers closed around the jagged lump in my pocket. "And what was with the handle? There was barely anything to grab."

I slowly revealed my chunky secret. We dissolved into hysterical giggles. It was official. We'd suffered our last Diana story. We could never go back.

CHAPTER 51

Francine for the Win

"I've got a different suggestion for tonight, Kel." Francine grinned at me over her teacup. "Let's go bar hopping! The Go-Go bars in the Patpong district are famous. You're entertained by girls dancing on stage wearing practically nothing." She paused to let that visual delight sink in. "It'd be fun to explore a completely new version of Bangkok, wouldn't it? However, we probably shouldn't go alone. I'll ask Pook to join us."

While ogling scantily dressed Go-Go girls wasn't on my list of Bangkok must-do's, I smiled and nodded. I knew nothing would come of it. Pook would never chaperone customers on such a mission. He was a studious shipper, not an inveterate barfly.

"I'll call him now, shall I?"

"He won't be awake yet, Mom. It's only 6 a.m."

Francine was in full on Madame Wasabi mode.

I watched in amusement as her face lit up when they spoke some hours later.

"Yes, Kelly's excited, too. We're both looking forward to experiencing another slice of Bangkok. Okay, thanks, Pook. See you at 8."

He rang back later that afternoon.

"Oh, that is unfortunate. Perhaps tomorrow night? No? How about Wednesday? I see. Well, we'll have to leave it for another trip then. Okay, our best to your father." My mother put the phone down slowly. "I'm sorry, Kel. Pook's dad needs help with some accounting problem."

Of course he did.

Francine flicked a lock of hair off her face. "Ah well. We'll opt for plan B."

Plan B?

"Kickboxing."

Oh, she was good. Not only did the wily Francine suspect that Pook might not come through, but she'd looked into options.

As we waited for our driver, she cheerfully informed the crowded hotel lobby that tonight would be a dream come true. Francine apparently "ached" to attend a kickboxing match ever since Prime Minister Trudeau experienced it on his '83 Thai trip.

First I'd heard of it.

When the Mercedes pulled up alongside the arena, our uniformed driver apologized for "having little English." Francine tugged up her sleeve and pointed to her watch.

"Please pick us up in one hour." She held up an index finger and repeated the request.

The driver misunderstood. He pocketed the keys and gestured for us to follow. We traipsed through the cavernous lobby and over to the ticket booth, where a young woman chatted with him in rapid Thai. As she grew ever more animated, I was beginning to think we were at the wrong venue until she suddenly rattled off the price for three tickets in perfect English. The driver was now our guest. But where was everyone else? Either we were extremely early or Thai kickboxing wasn't very popular.

All became clear when the driver hauled on a thick wooden door and we plunged into a different world; it was transformative. As my eyes slowly adjusted in the inky darkness, I made out a pair of wiry lads wearing nothing but baggy shorts and boxing gloves, scampering onto the boxing ring far below. The spectators numbered in the thousands. They erupted into a loud roar as the referee signaled the match was about to begin.

Everyone in our row fell silent as we took our seats. I immediately understood why. We were the only women present, at least in our section. Francine wasn't bothered. She whispered ecstatically, "Oh, Kel, isn't this marvelous!"

It was. We stayed a full hour. One match melted seamlessly into another and I gradually discerned some rule basics. Each match was limited to five three-minute rounds, with two-minute breaks in between. These forty-some-odd years later, I'm still in awe of the athletes and their whirling kicks.

When our chauffeur ushered us back to the car, we remained in the dark. If it was meant to be a "males only" night, how lucky were we? The experience remains a highlight of my six trips to Thailand, all thanks to a mother who refused to stay in her lane.

CHAPTER 52

The Ring Odyssey

Our Thai shipment arrived earlier than expected thanks
to Pook's efficiency. We rounded up Evelyn, Noah, Ed,
Susan and Beth, our core group of loyal "wreckers" and
eagerly got to work. However, the usual crowbar method was
instant overkill. The wooden tops peeled away like cheap nail
polish, revealing untold layers of soggy wrapping paper. All eight
crates had been compromised during their seven-thousand-mile
journey to Vancouver.

The garage soon smelled as if we were tramping through a bog
of damp soil and decaying leaves. Mold. Francine's number one
asthmatic trigger. She abandoned her post and hustled into the
hallway to triage the items once they'd been thoroughly cleaned
and dried.

Godfrey raided the linen cupboard. With the others now on
towel duty, Noah and I volunteered to dispose of the soupy wrapping material. Our initial attempts to carefully unspool it proved
ridiculously time consuming and we ended up just dumping the
pulpy lumps into the empty crates. The process was an unpleas-

ant, back-breaking slog and I was exhausted when I crawled into bed at midnight.

I dragged myself into FROG seven hours later and ignored the ringing phone as we weren't officially open for another three hours. When the calls persisted, I suspected it was Francine.

"Hi, Mom, what's up?"

"It's Noah. I'm a mess. I've lost my ring! My Grandpa's ring!"

As someone who frequently misplaces things, I knew not to insult the panicked soul by inquiring if he'd thoroughly checked every possible pocket and surface. Of course he had.

Think, Kelly, think.

"We washed up, Noah, just before dessert. Your ring is probably by the sink in the downstairs bathroom."

"Oh God, I hope so."

"When did you first notice it missing?"

"When I got home. It felt loose when I first dug into a crate so I shoved it in my jeans. When I got undressed it wasn't in my pocket. I can't remember putting it back on ..." Noah's voice trailed off.

Surely the ring wasn't lost among the god-forsaken pulpy detritus? We'd never find it, if so. But I couldn't tell him that. I had to help; it vanished on our watch.

"Okay, I'll ask Francine to check the sink and I'll find out what time the guys are picking up the crates."

The boss didn't mince words.

"It's not in either bathroom, Kel. I don't think there's a chance in hell you'll find it. It's just a mess outside. I'm so sorry. I'd offer to help but ..."

"The last thing we need is you out sick with asthmatic wheezing, Mom. If we don't find it by lunch, I'll call you. You can commiserate and help him through the loss."

Noah and I arrived at Tolmie Street to find the eight battered crates looking worse than I expected. Scattered helter-skelter in the driveway, they were piled high with soupy trash. The weather didn't help. It was a typical Vancouver day in January – chilly, drizzly and bleak. Exactly the conditions that David Duchovny, *The X-Files* actor, so publicly abhorred.

We quickly decided to divide and conquer. I appreciated Noah's willingness to tackle the largest crate. It was a tough go as we lapsed into a mindless dance of bending, scooping, palpating, unfurling and tossing. Our fingers were numb within minutes.

When Francine emerged at 9:30 to head into work, she hollered cheerful encouragement at Noah before sidling over to my crate.

"Dad could have pitched some paper into one of our garbage cans. Check them if this doesn't pan out," she whispered, before adding, "What a miserable job. Sorry, Kel. Call me."

I ached to trade places with her.

When Noah suggested we search the last three crates together, I couldn't fault his effort. He attacked the sodden heaps with as much energy as that of the very first.

"Stop," he barked some twenty minutes in. "Did you hear that?"

I froze. Nothing. Just the splats of rain falling on my hood.

"It was definitely metal. Stop and drop," he ordered.

We fell to the floor of the crate and pawed carefully through the sludge.

"Oh My God. I've got it!" Noah squealed.

I needed visual proof.

As Noah thrust the ring in my face, I realized just how very lucky he was to find it. The slim gold band pinched between his thumb and forefinger was tiny; its circumference slightly larger than a dime. I punched my fist in the air as he jammed it onto his baby finger.

"Thank you for your unending positivity, Kelly. I honestly thought it was lost forever."

Me, too.

We whooped and hugged with a joyful relief probably best understood by the likes of Frodo and Bilbo Baggins.

CHAPTER 53

Billie

After five years in the biz, I fully understood how antique shops were so much more than their inventory. They were hangouts, spots for folks to gather, enjoy some refreshments and feel truly appreciated. FROG was about to become just that for a lonely octogenarian nurse.

The elderly woman hovering in the doorway, mindful of dripping water onto the carpet, was the first person to venture in on that drizzly February afternoon.

"Would you be interested in a music box?" she called out in a voice quite thin.

"I'm sorry, dear. You need the shops across the street. Look around, we don't deal in things like that here," Francine breezily explained, whirling about like a KitchenAid stand mixer.

The stranger's face crumpled.

"However, you *are* in luck on the tea front. Kelly was just nipping out for some. Please join us, it's such a bitterly cold day," the boss rallied, grasping the need for a reboot.

As the woman toppled into a chair, Francine and I exchanged

worried looks. Why was she selling the music box? To get money for food?

I slipped on my coat and dashed out.

"You're one thirsty puppy today, Kelly," the friendly Granville Diner barista observed, noting my second order within the hour.

"Gotta revive a customer. Elderly," I barked, snatching up several sugar packets. Francine would be impressed with my foresight. She always extolled the virtues of "something sweet" when it came to exhaustion and shock.

I scurried back juggling a bag of muffins and a carryout tray of tea. While it was a relief not to spot an ambulance idling outside FROG, I wasn't fooled. Francine wouldn't be able to call 911 if she was feverishly thumping the stranger's chest.

The serenity inside was disorienting.

"Your mother would be running the hospital now if I'd been in charge, Kelly," our patient exclaimed.

I showered the discombobulated woman with sugar packets.

"What *are* you doing, Kelly? I am sorry, dear. Let me take those." Francine scooped them up before snatching up a tea. "Here, get this inside you, Billie," she soothed, glaring at me as if I was the addled one.

"No, thank you, Frankie, I just ate."

Francine nodded and reached for the bag.

"I'll have one. I'm starving."

I plucked it out of my mother's hands, mutely demanding some clarity.

"Billie was telling me about her job as the Director of Nursing at the Royal Jubilee Hospital in Victoria. Imagine how different my life might be if she'd been in charge when I was there."

I grappled to catch up. The story of Francine's brief nursing career didn't loom large in our family lore. We just knew that some nursing matron hit the roof when she caught our 18-year-old napping during bandage rolling duty. The nasty woman ordered Mom to work a double shift in the intensive care unit, and threatened further disciplinary measures should the critically ill patient die. When he unfortunately did, Matron yanked Mom's specialized training privileges. Unwilling to partake in an education that would now be "deadly dull," our mother quit. Bye-bye nursing career.

"Yes, I imagine life would be very different if I'd stuck with it," Francine murmured pensively.

"You could be flying yourself to a whistling competition this very minute!" the octogenarian chirped.

Talk about your classic non sequitur. Mom's new friend *was* loopy.

"My one true love married someone else, you see," she murmured coquettishly, drawing me in.

"When I lost him. I devoted my life to nursing, flying small planes and entering competitive whistling contests."

I began to see her appeal.

"That is, until..." Billie teased, ensuring she had our attention " ... Art's wife passed away. He came calling, we married and I retired. We bought a camper van and spent the next 15 years exploring Canada and the States."

"Wow. You're living the true fairytale, Billie," I cooed.

Her eyes filled with tears.

"I lost my Art to cancer just last month," she murmured, her face crumpling once again. "That's why I'm selling my music box. He gave it to me. It's time for another couple to enjoy it."

My throat closed and the usually modest hum of the overhead fluorescent lights thrummed defiantly, as if reprimanding me for upsetting this lonely soul. As usual, Francine recovered first. She shot me a look I immediately understood.

"Well, Art led you to us today." With me now nodding alongside like a maniacal bobblehead, she added, "We're here for you, dear. You are most welcome to drop by anytime."

Billie took Francine at her word.

The octogenarian became a firm FROG fixture, initially popping in once a day, either before or after lunching at a nearby restaurant. Newbies could be forgiven for mistaking her for a sales associate. Francine and I were delighted to witness her life take on more meaning, a fact reflected in her wardrobe. Initially digging into Art's closet, she slowly branched out into more feminine options. Francine introduced her to Mrs. King at Edward Chapman's, and that was it. Billie fully embraced the world of contemporary women's fashion.

As the frequency of her FROG visits ramped up to twice daily, so did Billie's pride. It refused to allow her to linger without a reason. She began to shower us with gifts sourced from the "on special" bin at the local drugstore. The variety was endless, ranging anywhere from nylons, batteries and matches, to soon-to-be expired delights like cookies, soup, pasta and chocolate. It was too much. We were agonizing over how to get her to stop when Billie suddenly switched to a different option.

"We won!" my mother shrieked over the phone on my day off.

"I'm sorry, what?"

"The lottery ticket!" Francine spluttered.

"Oh. Nice."

Mom always bought lottery tickets. I was more interested in the loose threads on my couch than her usual five-or-ten-dollar win.

"You clearly don't get it," Francine remonstrated. She began speaking as if I was a child. "Billie gave me a lottery ticket. I promised to give her half of any winnings." Her pace quickened.

"Well, we won big."

She had my full attention now.

"How big, Mom?"

"$1,000! She's absolutely thrilled with her $500."

Not bad for a one-dollar investment.

The big win cemented their bond. I remained on casual terms until a few months later when Billie bustled in, demanding to speak with Francine. When I informed her that the boss was regrettably out for lunch with a customer, she looked quite forlorn.

"Billie, I'm here for you," I broached tentatively.

I reached out for her hand and her shoulders slumped.

"I can't drive any more, Kelly. I failed my road test. My reflexes are too slow!" she blurted.

I couldn't understand the impact, I was too young. She really should be talking to Francine.

"Surely you can try again. Go back in a week or so and ask to redo it."

Billie tossed her license at me.

"At my age, I'm only allowed to take *one* test."

Well, this was awkward. I had nothing; there wasn't an appropriate response. How old was she anyway? I glanced at the license and froze.

"Billie, I can't believe it." The words tumbled out in a breathless squeak.

"I know. Art always said I had the reflexes of a youngster."

"You're *exactly* 49 years older than me! We share the same birthday!"

I whipped my driver's license out of my wallet and Billie's distress melted like candles on a cake. To hell with the failed road test. She'd found family.

CHAPTER 54

Tech Talk

"**K**eep your next six Tuesday nights free, Kel. I've registered for that introductory computer course," Francine announced while handing over my morning latte.

I was excited. We hoped to learn how a computer could benefit FROG. Francine and I giggled remembering the behemoth number she used 20 years earlier in her elective UBC Computer Science course. It took up an entire room and possessed huge wheels that spat out reams of cards. They'd changed a bit since then.

"Dad's joining us," Francine added.

Good. It'd be grand to have another raw newbie in the mix.

The high school computer lab boasted two laptops per table. Godfrey hustled us immediately to the back row. The average age of our classmates was around 50, with one noticeably younger person sitting two rows up. Her brunette bob looked familiar. I failed to place her before a tall and slightly stooped gentleman swept into the room, bristling with nervous energy. In his early 40s, he strode to the blackboard and printed "GIGABYTE" in huge chalk letters.

"As we all know, a gigabyte is two to the 30th power or 1,073,741,824 in decimal notation," he trumpeted.

I smothered a grin as Godfrey snorted, "Good God, Kel. Are we in the right class?"

Neglecting to share his name, our instructor spent the next twenty minutes blathering on in mysterious tech talk. It was as if someone had injected sleep serum into the heating ducts. With most folks yawning and slumped low in their chairs, the chances of it actually being an introductory class were pretty good.

"Excuse me, could we possibly get some hands-on work done tonight?" the familiar gal piped up bravely.

Bingo.

"Hey, Gayle!" I squealed.

My dental hygienist flashed me a quick eye roll as our teacher frowned at his watch.

"Fine. You may boot it up." No one stirred. "Turn it on," he ordered, his patience running thin. "But *DO NOT TOUCH* anything else."

Francine's jade bracelets jangled as she pressed the power button. Godfrey shot up his hand.

"How do I turn mine on? I can't find the power button. It's not where it should be."

"That's because you're sitting at a printer," Professor Nameless tonelessly advised.

The tension in the room melted like the ice in one of Bard's special cocktails. Godfrey acknowledged the collective laughter with a rueful smile and scooted his chair closer to mine. While we giggled like a pair of naughty school kids, Francine ignored us completely. She was in full-on student mode. As her fingers danced over the keyboard, Godfrey and I scrambled to catch up. We watched in wonder as the screen flickered and a golden cursor suddenly flashed to life.

Not ten minutes later, Francine suddenly sighed and shoved her glasses onto her forehead.

"What's up, Mom?"

"I'm blinded by the damn screen," she hissed impatiently before calling out, "Excuse me, Sir, is there any way to tone down the background? It's *very* harsh."

The instructor closed his eyes and took a deep breath. He'd pegged us as "the difficult family."

"Tilt the angle of the screen. Now, Class, who knows what DOS stands for?"

No one stirred.

As he launched into a dreary explanation, Francine soldiered on, pecking at the keyboard with her right hand while shading her eyes with the left.

"I'll have to bring sunglasses next time," she muttered, finally noticing me. "Don't just sit there, Kel! Play with the keyboard. It's just like a typewriter."

I lost myself in the fluid wonder of it all. My fingers flew and sentences miraculously appeared on the screen.

"That's pretty cool, eh, Dad?"

"I suspect some of you are keen to do some World Wide Web searching," the instructor intoned.

Whatever was he on about now? I turned to snigger with Godfrey but stopped cold. The good doctor was leaning against the wall, with both hands clasped behind his head and his eyes closed, evoking the, "I work in the back of my wife's shop" episode. I offered to switch seats so he could have a little keyboard action, but his eyelids fluttered dismissively. Godfrey was done.

"I'm sorry, but I *must* speak. I believe it would be truly beneficial for you, Sir, to learn what everyone hopes to get out of the class. Could we please just share why we're all here?" Not waiting for an answer, Francine surged on. "I'll start, shall I? I'm Frankie Robinson and I run an Asian antiques shop on South Granville with my daughter Kelly. We're hoping to learn how to streamline our inventory and accounting efforts." She smiled encouragingly to the man directly in front of her. He stirred and dutifully shared, "I'm a contractor. I'd like to use a computer to keep track of my accounts payable and payroll." And around the room it went. When the last person finished sharing, the room was infused with happy anticipation. Surely now, armed with such knowledge, the instructor could provide more practical information.

Professor Nameless's face remained frozen in neutral.

"Your homework is to become familiar with the keyboard. Hide your hands under something like a tea towel or some newspaper. Once you're comfortable locating the correct keys without looking, you're to type a letter to a friend."

The collective groan conveyed the obvious. The majority were already keyboard proficient.

"Excuse me. What if we don't have access to a computer?" My mother queried.

His jaw dropped.

"You're taking a computer class without access to a computer?"

"Yes."

The fellow rubbed his hands over his face.

"Do you have a typewriter?"

"Yes. It's a lovely electric one with automatic white-out," Francine crowed. She was especially proud of that feature.

"Practice on it, Ma'am, practice on it."

Gayle and I had lots to talk about at my next dental appointment. She also dropped out of the Tuesday night "Introduction To The Computer" course after just one class, and we wondered how many, if any, returned for the second.

CHAPTER 55

Annexation

Paul seemed pleased with FROG's 1988 Year End results. As the accountant patiently walked us through the highlights, Francine struggled a bit with the financial-speak. But nevermind. The guy knew his audience. He answered my questions in ways we both could understand, and assured us the business was doing well. However, he agreed we had a problem. Our Granville Street shop was bursting at the seams. With two large shipments arriving soon, we needed a major pivot.

Francine came up with a clever solution: a pop-up shop. It would offer mostly the "dead inventory," the pieces that had lingered for over six months, at greatly reduced prices. Securing my willingness to run it, she arranged for a one-month lease of the recently vacated stationery store located just two doors up.

The heavy lifters arrived at dawn on moving day. As I triaged, Bert and today's genial flunky, Bobby, began hauling pieces down the back passage connecting the two businesses.

Needle-thin like FROG, the temporary space lacked the window ledge and display platform. As the lads eased a giant mizuya in front of the window, the showroom plunged into darkness, immediately transporting me back to the day we shut down Fiona's travel agency. Nothing would sell under these conditions.

I sorted out a game plan. All the smalls up front, the massive bits towards the back. Should someone request more advantageous viewing, there was always the sidewalk. By morning's end, we'd created a charming rabbit warren complete with several narrow tunnels carved throughout the inventory. The office and bathroom were designated holding pens, and there wasn't a hope in hell of accessing the back door, thanks to the stack of neatly folded screens.

"Call us if there's a cave-in, Kelly! We'll send in a backhoe," Bert declared, half-joking.

The movers tapped out and I tore the brown paper off the windows, slapped up the large "Frankie Robinson Sale" banner, taped a small note on the door announcing tomorrow's opening, and locked up. Time to check on FROG.

"We can breathe again, Kel," Francine crowed, whirling about.

It was true. FROG looked elegant and inviting. I wanted to curl up on the elevated platform for a wee nap. But the boss was eager to view our temporary annex.

"Christ, we could open a *third* shop," Francine observed, peering in from the sidewalk.

"It's a damn nightmare," I replied.

A nightmare it was. Many customers simply couldn't grasp the new setup. The inventory switch had been too quick. Their bewilderment ranged from, "What the heck? Where'd you put the cards?" to "I need help with ordering my wedding invitations but where can we sit?" and the ever popular, "Do you still carry gift wrap?"

This could be a very long month.

I was locking up early on the third day when an Honorable Member of Parliament entered the shop. She represented my federal electoral district in Ottawa and I recognized her immediately. I donned my coat, assuming she was looking for cocktail napkins or curly ribbon.

"Kelly? Your mother suggested I check out your screens. Can you show me some smaller ones?"

"Screens? Small? Yes, yes! Come!"

I shed the coat and dialed down the enthusiasm. We spent a pleasant half hour viewing various options out on the sidewalk, and I closed my first sale. I couldn't wait to tell Francine.

The trickle of sales slowly increased, thanks to word of mouth and our mailout and phone call efforts. My spirits lifted when Julia James stopped by at the end of the second week.

"I have some news to share, Kelly."

As the flight attendant wove her way to my makeshift desk, I broke out in anticipatory goosebumps. Julia's updates were always a treat.

"My bowel cancer is back."

Wait. What? This was the first I'd even heard of it.

"It was in remission for nine years and now it's back. However, my doctor and I have worked out battle plans. The first of my chemo rounds is done and I should be able to keep flying throughout the rest," she explained while keenly surveying the shop.

"I am so sorry, Julia," I croaked, now desperate for Francine.

"No. Please don't." Her fluttering hands fought off sympathy. "I've come in for a spirit booster. Show me everything."

I covertly studied Julia as we minced our way through the still teetering piles. She was radiant; there wasn't a hint of illness. Nor was there a trace of self-pity, just a stoic "carry-on-as-usual" attitude. Her eyes lit up when they fell upon a late nineteenth century, Chinese footed porcelain bowl. Eight inches across, the white glaze was dotted with small brown bats and large robust peaches.

"I can't believe you still have this, Kelly! I've dreamt about it. Just look at that design. Bats and peaches are both symbols of longevity, right? A double dose of fortune. I'll take it."

There wasn't a moment to ruminate on the cancer diagnosis. Immediately after seeing Julia out, I sold a small table and the last of the wooden elephant bells, and then Billie slipped in. My heart sank. She'd want to share every detail of her new pacemaker and I didn't have the patience to listen. I was gasping for coffee and had five customers waiting to talk to me.

"Hi Billie. I'm a bit swamped at present. I know Mom would love to see you."

"I've just come from there. She asked me to tell you she's bored." Billie looked around impatiently. "I've got something very special to show you when you're free."

As if offering up their seats to the octogenarian on a crowded bus, a couple smiled and left. Billie stared down the remaining three, one of whom happened to be a favorite designer of mine.

"We're fine, Kelly. You look after your friend," he murmured, shuffling his clients toward the back.

Mollified, Billie thrust a black transistor at my ear. It was slightly larger than a pack of cards and I wondered if she was giving it to me.

"Have a listen," she demanded, snapping it on. It wasn't tuned to a station and the static blast damn near deafened me.

"Did you hear them?" Billie asked, quivering with anticipation. I shook my head impatiently.

"I'll turn it up."

Great. The piercing shriek already made my molars ache. I

searched her face for clues, anything that would help me ascertain the goal.

"There! *That*."

Nothing discernable. Again, just … crickets.

Billie tutted loudly and jammed the cacophonous torture machine right against my ear.

"Everyone be quiet! Listen carefully, Kelly, for some clicking sounds," she admonished.

I shut my eyes and concentrated as the trio obediently fell silent. A series of distinct clicks were embedded in the static. They were faint but patently regular. I nodded.

"You heard them? Great. Guess what they are."

"Sorry, no clue." I replied, dearly hoping the others wouldn't leave.

"They're my *heartbeats!* The radio is picking them up through the pacemaker. Isn't that marvelous?" Billie exclaimed, as eager as Marie Curie championing radiation.

I didn't dare ask how she discovered this marvel, innately understanding that wasn't the point.

"Huh, that's quite the party trick, Billie, now if you'll excuse me."

My frustration grew as the octogenarian turned toward the others.

"Do you know Frankie, Kelly's mother?"

The designer nodded.

"She runs their original store two shops down. It's called 'Frankie Robinson Oriental Gallery.' You should check it out after shopping here," she advised, winking at me. "But first, hear me out. Kelly, it's not about performing party tricks. It's about offering comfort to folks with pacemakers. How many patients know how to check their pulse rate? Very few. But, armed with a transistor like this, all they need to do is turn it on and listen. Come, check it out."

As the trio eagerly lined up for the transistor experience, I saw Billie as they now did. For these brief minutes, she was once again, the Director of Nursing, in charge and respected. Who was I to snuff out this joy? I eased away and welcomed a new set of walk-ins.

Billie and her Transistor Heartbeat Tracker proved to be quite the godsend over the next few weeks. She kept folks entertained, freeing me up to chat with other customers. By the end of our pop-up tenure, we were very pleased with the inventory turnover. However, I wouldn't be opening my own antiques shop soon. If ever. The incessant quibbling over prices and questioning of authenticity were beyond tiresome without Francine and her plethora of personalities to dilute the impact. Yes, she was just a mere two doors down, but it wasn't remotely the same.

CHAPTER 56

About that Tarp

When I mentioned the possibility of taking a two-week summer break tootling about Eastern Canada with John, Francine happily gave me the time off. However, she did harbor one regret, according to her diary notation: "I just wish it was their honeymoon."

We didn't keep her in suspense for long. Two months later, when John and I decided to get engaged, he insisted on enlisting our parents' blessing before making the big announcement. He told his parents first. I was surprised and delighted by his mother's reaction.

"Mom's urging me to include you when I go looking for a ring, Kel. So, if I get the green light from your folks," he smiled, playfully crossing his fingers, "we'll book it to the jewelers. Is that okay with you?"

It surely was.

We settled on the following Saturday. John would pop over to Tolmie Street before work and then we'd head to the jewelers. Of course, Francine would give me the time off. We were golden.

Or so we thought.

"Thank God you're still home!" My mother sounded frantic.

I peeked at the clock on my bedside table. Of course I was still home. It was barely dawn. FROG wouldn't open for hours.

"Osler's missing, Kel."

Osler was missing? Oh, no. A littermate of Angus, the McKenzie's pup, the one-year-old Black Labrador Retriever had never escaped before. Could he find his way home? I sat up as Francine gasped out an explanation.

"We went down to the beach and Osler smelled something irresistible. He suddenly took off. Dad is beside himself. By some miracle, John dropped by for his tarp and joined the hunt. I've told the regular dog walkers, but we need your help, too. Please."

Did Mom seriously believe that John would reclaim a tarp at *dawn*? It would have to be *quite* the emergency. His dad's company had heaps of tarps. And poor Dad. He would be devastated. Godfrey and the dog, named after the physician Sir William Osler, were quite inseparable. Good grief, what timing. Truly. The last thing we needed was for our special day to be inexorably linked to the tragic "Goodbye-Osler" day. We had to find the dog. I dressed quickly and carefully, knowing it might not be practical to return home and change for work.

The Spanish Banks beach is about a mile-and-a-half long. John and Dad would have it covered. Something told me to head to Jericho beach. I cruised along the moderately busy 4th Avenue, and turned off at Alma Street, toward the ocean, and drove slowly along the deserted roads.

I felt I was dreaming when I spotted Osler five minutes later just up ahead, sauntering along the sidewalk as carefree as a well-fed toddler. He was heading in the wrong direction and at least two miles from Tolmie Street. I screeched to the curb and hollered his name. The sand-encrusted pup leapt joyfully onto the front seat and settled down as if we did this routinely.

I threw my arms around him.

"Let's deliver you safely home, Osler. I'll drop you off and slip away."

He thumped his tail in acknowledgement.

Unfortunately, Francine was home alone. She leaned frantically over the back deck railing the second we pulled up.

"Thank you for coming over so quickly, Kelly. I'm stuck here in case a neighbor brings Osler back. John came by to get his tarp and then shot off to help. I do hope he met up with Dad," she hollered, her voice thick with worry.

I simply opened Osler's door. He dashed out and shot up the outside steps that led to the deck, rendering Francine speechless.

"He was down by the Jericho Tennis Club, Mom, going in the completely wrong direction. He's caked in sand but otherwise well." The words tumbled out in a rush. I still couldn't quite believe my luck.

"Oh thank God. Your father will be so happy. You must stay so you can explain how you found him. What a bad boy, Osler." Francine's actions defied her words as she sank down and embraced the wriggling Black Lab.

We settled into the deck chairs to await the return of the others and Osler flopped down at our feet. He was exhausted. He had quite a morning and it wasn't yet 7:30. I did worry Mom would mention John's sudden need for the tarp, but thankfully, my miraculous find eclipsed everything.

The men arrived back some ten minutes later.

"It's okay, Geoff. Kelly found him! He's safely home!" Francine rang out as I opened the gate and Osler rocketed down the stairs into the arms of his astonished owner.

"You gave us quite the scare, old boy." Godfrey hugged him tightly before standing up. "Come on, time for crackers," he crooned, grabbing the dog's collar.

This was crackers. Time to leave.

I nodded at John as we gathered in the kitchen.

"You scared the hell out of me, running off like that, you little bugger." Dad lovingly ruffled Osler's velvety black ears before reaching into the gigantic bin of animal crackers. He bought them in bulk, refusing to believe they were meant for human consumption. John stared in alarm as Godfrey began tossing the crackers by the handful onto the kitchen floor.

"Wherever did you find him, Kel? We looked everywhere, didn't we, John?"

"Yup. We went up one end of the beach to the other."

I spat out an abbreviated Cliff Notes-type version and jangled my keys. John smothered a smile but my father was oblivious to my discomfort. He simply stared at the dog in wonderment.

"All the way to Jericho! What a hike, Osler. You must be exhausted. Eat up, there's a good fellow."

"We could *all* do with a hearty breakfast, I think. How about some bacon and eggs? Kel, you'll stay?" Francine spoke over the dog's incessant crunching.

My pulse raced as John made a noise that could be excused as a simple dry cough but I knew better.

"Uh, no thanks, Mom. I think I'll just slip away now and get ready for work," I mumbled, scraping back my chair.

"Nonsense, Kelly. You look perfect just as you are. I know you haven't eaten. Now pour yourselves some coffee, and I'll make breakfast," Francine insisted.

I wasn't in the least bit hungry. My hands clutched the coffee cup so tightly it was a wonder it didn't shatter. This was meant to be John's sacred time with my folks. I normally could enlist Dad's help but today he was hopeless. The man only had eyes for his dog, who in turn, was oblivious to all but the unexpected second breakfast. Osler inhaled the scattered crackers, all the while dispensing sand like an avid gardener topdressing his lawn.

The aroma of fried eggs and crisp bacon provided a momentary distraction, reminding me of those early morning business meetings with Peter, which we thankfully no longer needed. I caught John's eye and he swiftly shook his head. Everything was on hold until we ate.

When Francine called us to the table, Dad took his usual place at the head and insisted that Osler sit alongside.

"I am not taking my eyes off of you, boy," he vowed, shuffling his chair closer. He leaned down and crooned, "You're going to get a bath right after breakfast. You've brought home half the beach."

Always a fan of the bath, Osler cocked his head and happily swished his tail, immune to his owner's admonishment. I dared not look at John.

The bizarre disconnect continued throughout the meal.

"It's a good thing we redid the window yesterday, Kel. I've got Evan coming in to see the *satsuma* (Japanese earthenware pottery) vase. I think Brenda's also coming in to have a look at the netsuke. She needs a gift for her sister's birthday."

While Francine was preparing for the day ahead, Godfrey couldn't move on.

"I do wish you could talk and tell me what you got up to, old boy. Why did you go off like that? I was worried sick about you."

While Osler rolled over onto his back for belly rubs, and John listened politely, nodding when applicable, I choked down what I considered to be an appropriate amount of food.

"Oh, Kel, slow down. We don't have to leave for another hour.

NEVER, NEVER, HARDLY EVER

Top up your coffees," Francine remonstrated, turning to John. "I do apologize for not giving you my full attention earlier, dear. So, you need the tarp?"

John and I locked eyes across the table. I tried to convey my discomfort at being the classic interloper. He nodded and my resolve hardened. Okay, enough. We were adults. It was time to stand up for us both and walk out. But then John switched gears. Or perhaps I'd simply misinterpreted the nod. He gave a little shrug and smiled, silently granting me leave to stay. Everything faded to black as he cleared his throat and stood.

"Frankie and Geoff, I need to ask you something."

"Of course, you can take the tarp, John. It's fine. The roofer should be here any day now. Sit, sit." Francine flapped her hands impatiently. "Geoff can help haul it down in a bit."

"It's not about the tarp, actually," he declared firmly.

I had to give it to him. John was the picture of grace and calm. You'd think he was proposing another round of buttered toast.

"I'd like to borrow Kelly for an hour or so this morning."

"It was amazing how she found our Osler, wasn't it, Dad?"

Good Lord. This was absolute torture. Francine wasn't remotely following the plot and Godfrey was off with the fairies. Poor John. No wonder he was leading with the ring selection concept.

"Utterly amazing, Francine," John replied slowly, answering for my father. He clearly grasped the need to speak plainly to my parents, almost as if they were learning English. "I need Kelly to help me choose an engagement ring."

Francine looked at first confused and then profoundly sad. Who was the lucky girl if not her daughter? It was all I could do to remain silent.

Her head swiveled, and as she took in our radiant smiles, her eyes filled with tears. Francine got it. Finally. She hugged John and then stumbled over to me.

"I love Kelly," John declared, his voice catching slightly. My heart went out to him as he steadied himself. "It would make me so very happy if you would give us your blessings to marry."

A veil suddenly dropped and it was as if I was looking directly into his soul. Everything shifted. My throat closed as I realized in that second how incredibly blessed I was to witness such a raw, unguarded and genuine declaration.

"Oh, John, that's absolutely wonderful. We couldn't be happier for you both," Francine managed just above a whisper.

And my father's response to this heartfelt request for his youngest daughter's hand? He sighed, and looking besottedly at his favorite, declared, "I love you, dear Osler. With all of my being."

Jesus. Was the good doctor suffering from a stroke?

"For the love of God, Geoff. *LISTEN!* John is asking for our blessings to marry Kelly."

Dad froze as if he'd been slapped. His face became a canvas of conflicting emotions, transitioning from startlement to sadness, then sheepishness, and finally sheer joy. He reached out and firmly gripped John's hand with both of his.

"I could not be more delighted," he whispered. He glanced at Francine and smiled.

"You have our most heartfelt blessings, John. You're both very special. May you have a long and happy marriage."

I began crying as Dad enfolded me in a hug.

"Thank you, Geoff and Francine. Your approval means everything to me," John replied, his voice once again catching. My parents fell silent in acknowledgement of this special future son-in-law and I was grateful that John had his moment, despite my awkward presence.

Osler scrambled to his feet. Enough. It was time for his bath.

"What a morning, eh?" My father exchanged meaningful looks with both of us, shook his head slightly, and then grinned the impish smile I loved so much.

"Now about that tarp ..."

CHAPTER 57

The Honeymoon Period

"Welcome to our fabulous Honeymoon Suite," the bellboy announced, opening the door with a flourish.

Welcome to the Moulin Rouge boudoir, more like. The circular canopy bed, which could easily sleep six, was awash with pillows of all sizes. Dozens of tiny cubes reminiscent of licorice allsorts were sprinkled among the gigantic shams and King-sized pillows. All in a cranberry satin. As was the taut bedspread. A thick curtain of golfball-sized, crimson cotton balls, strung together from the metal canopy cross bars, provided an illusion of privacy.

"A double love bubble," the bellboy chimed in as he caught me staring at the gigantic round mirror affixed overhead.

The alcove directly across from the bed was out of the 1950s. I could easily picture a Hollywood starlet, sitting upon the narrow tufted bench, her legs tucked under the ivory-colored, spindly legged table, gazing at her reflection in the large tri-fold vanity mirror trimmed with white, bulbous lights.

"For the makeup application," the bellboy needlessly advised.

"Kel, you *need* to come and check out the bathroom," my mother suddenly hollered.

"Yes, it makes us most proud," the hotel employee enthused, thankfully not picking up on her sarcasm.

This room was triple the size of FROG's bathroom, and boasted a cavernous bathtub equipped with an extraordinary number of mysterious taps and spouts.

"Christ. One needs a rope ladder to climb safely in and out," Francine observed.

"And now, please, daughter's room."

The bellboy called us back into the bedroom and pointed to a sliding pocket door cleverly hidden in the wall opposite the windows. He tugged on a small circular handle, but the door refused to budge.

"I must work out more," he chuckled, giving it another tug.

The door lurched open with a murderous shriek, revealing an airless coat closet, containing a hastily assembled gurney-like bed outfitted with worn sheets and a wafer-thin pillow. A hefty flashlight rested on the floor.

"Should daughter wish to read, the flashlight won't disturb Mommy," the bellboy explained happily.

"Lovely. This will suit us nicely, thank you," Francine interrupted, holding out a ₩5,000 South Korean bill. A tip then worth about five Canadian dollars.

We burst into giggles the second the door whispered shut behind him.

"Won't I have fun in my cubby reading by flashlight?" I chortled.

"There's room in my bed for both of us, Kel."

I rolled my eyes.

"I wouldn't sleep a wink with that mirror overhead, are you kidding?"

"Well, there's always the wading pool in the bathroom."

"No, thanks, those taps are scary. I'll stick with the cubby, Mom. It'll be cozy. Perhaps you could spare a pillow or six?"

As Francine looked at the mound of cushions and then back at me, we started laughing again.

"It couldn't be more different from the last room." Mom managed between gasps.

No, it couldn't.

We spent the previous night, our first ever in Korea, in the same hotel, in what was surely known as their "Tiny Room From Hell." The wedge-shaped, windowless room was just big enough for the twin beds. I had to vault over Francine's to get into mine as they were squashed into the widest end with just a hair's width separating them. Judging by the musty smell, no one had occupied the room for a long time, if ever.

Francine had no trouble sleeping. She skipped over her Gentle Puff stage and landed directly on Squeegeeing. However, thanks to the proximity of the twins, I simply reached out and tapped her shoulder and the snoring eased. For a good five minutes at a time. After three solid hours of sleep, I awoke to a cheerful, "Time to get up, Kel! I've got news. See you at breakfast."

I felt reborn after a shower and when I entered the restaurant, Francine waved from a far corner.

"My news can wait. Order something filling. It's going to be a long day," my mother advised, tucking back into her platter of blueberry pancakes.

I ordered two fried eggs and toast, and impatiently slurped my coffee in the enforced silence before Francine finally finished eating.

"Okay, first of all, I'll be bruised for days from your incessant prodding," she admonished, rubbing her shoulders gently. "And second, we needn't survive another night in that godforsaken hellhole. We're getting a different room!"

I whooped, disturbing the woman at the next table.

"Sorry!" Francine and I apologized.

When the elderly woman gently smiled and resumed reading her paper, I envied her patience. She'd probably gotten more than three hours sleep, lucky gal.

"Anyways, when the front desk clerk spoke minimal English, we figured out a way to communicate through drawings. I started sketching a cramped triangular wedge containing two beds and a frowning stick figure on each, and finished by crossing out the lot with a huge X."

"Wow. Clever, Mom."

"Oh, just wait. There's more, believe me." She took a sip of tea before resuming. "I flipped the paper over and drew an expansive square-shaped room containing two large beds and a beaming stick figure on each, as well as a window blessed with billowing curtains. When I plastered that with a gigantic tick, the chap actually laughed. It was delightful. After a few tense minutes of fierce tippy-tapping on his computer, he added another gigantic tick."

"What? That's so fun, Mom."

"Right? But he wasn't finished! He produced another piece of paper and drew a huge round clock with its hands at 3. He tapped the drawing and said, 'Back here at 3. New room, same price.'" She sat back and scratched her head. "Can you believe it?"

Yes. If anyone could do it, our Francine could.

"Here's to a decent night's sleep," I saluted, raising my coffee cup.

"Amen to that, Kel. The hostess just told me the hotel is full. I'm curious to see where he'll put us."

New room, same price? Wow.

The room sorted, we were excited to case out the shopping opportunities. Thanks to Fiona's efficiency, we were staying in the Insa-dong district, only ten minutes from downtown Seoul. It was known for its antique shops.

However, with no contacts of any kind, Francine and I were flying blind. After thirty minutes of aimless roaming, we discovered nothing but dozens of athletic shoe stores. Our moods weren't improved by the chilly weather. Large fluffy snowflakes were settling on our shoulders, scarves and hair.

"Does this intersection seem awfully familiar to you?" Francine finally asked.

It did. We were wandering in circles.

"This is ridiculous, Kelly. We're going to freeze out here with nothing to show for it. I'm getting help."

My mother trotted over to the youthful, whistle-toting policeman directing traffic from a raised concrete mound. I winced as she tugged on his sleeve.

"Excuse me. Can you tell us where we can find *old* furniture? Not new. *Old.*" Francine brandished a crisp, multi-folded map and stabbed at it with her finger.

Startled, the officer jumped, expelling the whistle.

"I do apologize. Can you show me? Old furniture?"

I relaxed a little as the gentleman edged aside to give her more room. Francine gesticulated as they huddled on the tiny traffic island. The cop suddenly blew an ear-piercing blast comparable to the mystery bird in Amy's Kitsilano apartment, and all traffic obediently halted. He stepped off the curb and motioned for us to follow.

"Sweet Jesus, Mom. Are we off to jail?"

She pretended not to hear.

We arrived at a dreary, windowless building after ten minutes of brisk walking. I held back when he motioned for us to enter. Francine started this, let her take the reins. She spluttered in annoyance and bustled inside.

Several uniformed officers sat warming themselves around a pot-bellied stove in the middle of the small room. Our man spoke briefly to the eldest officer, nodded a quick farewell and slipped back outside. Francine's look of alarm was most gratifying.

"Where are you from?" the proxy asked, his bushy eyebrows glowering.

"Canada. I assure you we've done nothing wrong, sir. We are simply looking for old furniture for our shop. Our shop in Vancouver. Canada." Francine babbled.

The pot-belly gang perked up.

"Ben Johnson!" someone called out, referring to the disgraced Canadian runner who was stripped of his 100 meter gold medal at the Seoul Olympics almost two years earlier.

"Yes, that Ben, that Canada!" I chimed in.

"Yes, runner Ben. She also runs," my mother declared, pointing at me. "But not today. Today we are looking for old furniture. Can you help us?"

After an awkward few minutes in which no one spoke, the senior officer suddenly stood up. Everyone stirred as he pulled on a jacket, clamped on his hat and beckoned us to follow. Where were we off to now?

Francine shrugged.

"God only knows. But we couldn't be in safer company, Kel," she decreed loudly, perhaps to reassure herself as well as me.

Lingering concerns of being hauled off to some remote jail vanished after the twenty-minute stroll. We were outside a visual treat. Stacks of chests of all sizes and varieties could be seen piled high through the large windows of an actual store.

"This gentleman sells genuine antique furniture and new pieces made from old wood. He'll treat you right." With that, the angel tipped his hat and headed back toward the station.

"Oh, Kel." Francine's eyes sparkled as she took in the surroundings. It was quite promising; more warehouse than showroom.

"New accommodation and now this. Nicely done, Mom. We'd have neither without you," I admitted through chattering teeth.

The shopkeeper, Mr. Kim, a genial fellow in his early 50s, offered us tea, as well as fluffy towels for our damp hair and shoes. We warmed up quickly and Francine explained the situation.

"Ah, you were escorted by my brother-in-law. Doesn't say much, but he's got a heart of gold," Mr. Kim replied.

Pleased to learn that we had some knowledge of his merchandise, he volunteered to guide us on a brief tour. We passed through the small showroom into the large warehouse we'd seen from the street. Mr. Kim began pointing out exquisite contemporary pieces created using salvaged wood of persimmon, paulownia and pine, as well as several authentic antiques. It was difficult to tell them apart.

"Do you know why most of the Korean chests have carved stands or legs?" he asked.

"I'm guessing that it's either to make them look like they're floating or because it makes the lower pieces easier to access," Francine offered.

I hadn't a clue.

"Good guesses, but no. It was to raise them up from the heated floors. Our heated flooring system is called 'ondol.' We light a fire and as the smoke travels through special passages under the floors it warms them up. The smoke escapes through a chimney and the floors stay warm for a long time."

"Why are the *bandaji* (clothing or blanket chest) doors often so small and the cavity so cavernous?" I now felt emboldened to ask. It was something I'd long wondered about.

"Korean clothes were not hung but folded and piled on top of each other. The small entry allows for careful and thoughtful placement," he explained easily.

His assistant Sylvie, a bright spark of about my age, called him to the phone, leaving Francine and I free to wander about. We admired the extensive collection of wooden bowls and utensils, book chests, folk-paintings, wedding gift boxes, and porcelains of every imaginable description, and were delighted to tick several items off customers' wish lists. A small chest with butterfly decorated hinges for Maisie, a Korean wedding duck for Conrad and a small box with a folding mirror for Sophie. We also selected several other small chests, as well as folk-paintings and porcelain.

After we arranged for payments and shipping, Mr. Kim insisted on taking us to lunch at his favorite restaurant. I was relieved when Francine thoroughly enjoyed the hot pot loaded with kimchi, green vegetables, mushrooms and tofu. No need for me to consume a second lunch today.

"I would be happy to drive you to your hotel," Mr. Kim offered as the server cleared the last of our plates.

"We'd love that. I don't know if we could find our way back on foot," Francine admitted.

Our new friends grimaced when they learned where we were staying.

"They've been talking for years about doing a massive renovation. It's long overdue," Sylvie revealed before cautiously asking, "How's your room?"

CHAPTER 58

Coincidence and Conspiracy

"It's happened again, Kel."

I didn't respond. There was no point. Francine wouldn't offer up another word until she'd lovingly tucked the last of her precious Thai glossy shopping bags into the inside pocket of her suitcase, where they'd remain forgotten for months.

"I've had another premonition," she finally clarified.

"Ugh, not *more* rubber chickens, Mom?"

Francine's lifelong phobia of snakes left her unable to even hear the word and she insisted we employ the "rubber chickens" euphemism. Mom's spidey-sense had been on full alert since Seoul. It was uncanny. Each time she dispatched me on a scouting mission, I encountered at least one snake charmer squatting alongside his writhing basket.

"No, the premonition was about a person this time, thankfully. Robert Sheldon. I think we're going to run into him."

That stopped me short. We were flying home today from Bangkok, Robert's adopted city.

"I hope I'm wrong."

Me, too. When we last saw the consignor, some three months ago, he was as endearing as ever. He continued to have only one topic. Himself.

It took us ages to get to the airport thanks to the chaotic morning rush hour, and when we finally made it through check-in and into security, I'd forgotten all about the prophecy.

"Over there! Look!" Francine suddenly squeaked.

Sweet Jesus. It was official. My mother had super powers. Just one lineup over, sporting a pair of pants so yellow they'd sour taste buds, was the man himself. Robert Sheldon.

"Christ! Hide!" I hissed, shrinking in behind her as if I were three.

Francine crossed her arms above her head as if waving home a distressed aircraft.

"Robert! Robert Sheldon!"

He recognized us immediately.

"You won't believe me, Robert, but just this morning, I had the premonition that we'd see you!"

He smirked and rubbed his hands together.

"It must be *quite* the hefty consignment check for you to come all this way! I'll wait for you outside!"

I couldn't stop staring. He'd lost so much weight, his teeth were positively equine.

"Are you okay, Robert?" my mother inquired once we'd cleared security.

"It's nothing, Frankie. Just my silly heart acting up again."

"Buddy, that's not something you want to ignore," I blurted.

"Nothing to worry about, dear," he assured me. "My beautiful bride takes excellent care of *moi*." He caught us peering behind him. "Oh, Juliette's not here. She's at home with her brother. He's living with us now. I'm just off to Hong Kong to renew my visa."

Robert was on our flight. Of course he was.

"And you're feeling well enough?" Francine persisted as we slowly made our way to the departure gate.

"Absolutely." He gulped lungfuls of air as if to prove it. "Honestly, you've nothing to worry about. I'm royally spoiled. Check it out. This tote is loaded with the wife's homemade protein packs. She makes them just for me."

As he held up the pale blue sports bag, the effort proved too much. He swayed and grabbed at an armrest to steady himself.

Francine messaged me with her eyes. We had an hour to kill. The fellow needed to sit.

"Let's catch up, shall we?"

She claimed the nearest available trio of seats without waiting for confirmation.

"Grab my tote, dear," Robert commanded, eager to reclaim the balance of power.

I scooped up the feather-light bag. The beautiful bride had packed just the essentials. Matching my gait to Robert's, we doddered over to join Francine.

"So how much is the check, ladies?"

"Uh, there isn't one. We've been on a buying trip for the store, Robert."

"Huh. I love my life."

I bit down on my cheek as he began to tick off his achievements.

"I've got a young, pretty wife who'll do anything for me, a brother-in-law who's happy to entertain her, and a home staffed with servants."

He drummed his fingers along his bony knee caps, loftily asserting, "Vancouver does nothing but rain. I honestly don't know why anyone would choose to live there."

Francine's face soured. Like me, she ached to remind him that he'd still be languishing in Vancouver if not for his late mother. I'd also love to ask about the multiple wives and the reasoning behind the citrus-colored trousers. But there was no point. Such comments and queries would only bounce off Robert like a handful of Nerf darts.

While the verbal diarrhea rolled on unabated, a well-placed "yes" tossed in with the odd, "I see" was all he required in terms of a response. The effect was soporific. I jumped when the loud-speaker crackled to life with the pre-boarding announcement.

"That's me! Keep selling, ladies. You never know when I'll pop in for a check," Robert smirked, before hauling himself onto his feet and slowly shuffling forward.

"Jesus, he's insufferable. The man doesn't even know we're on the same flight," I grumbled.

"Be kind, Kel. I don't think he's long for this world," Francine tutted. "He may be wealthy, but as Dad says, 'Ya ain't got nothing if you ain't got your health.'"

True. Billie had more get up and go than him.

The weeks turned into months with nary a peep from Robert. When his Aunt Dorothy dropped by in early December, we knew she'd been sent in to collect a nice Christmas bonus for her nephew.

"Welcome. How lovely to see you. I'll get Kelly to tally up the figures," Francine sang out.

"No, please. That can wait. I have some unfortunate news," the octogenarian intoned.

Francine and I glanced at each other. Now what?

"I'm sorry to inform you that my nephew Robert has passed away."

I felt and said … nothing.

Francine murmured, "Perhaps it's for the best."

The old gal looked more puzzled than gratified and my mother rushed to explain.

"He didn't look at all well when we bumped into him at the Bangkok airport a few months ago."

Dorothy still wasn't grasping it.

"He was having those heart problems again!" Mom explained in the voice she usually reserved for long distance calls.

The aunt's face cleared.

"There's no need to shout, dear. And no, it wasn't his heart. I'm afraid it was something far worse than that." Lifting her chin, she soldiered on. "My nephew was murdered."

Excuse me?

"Four men broke into his bedroom in the middle of the night and shot him."

The floor heaved as I envisioned a Charles Manson-Sharon Tate blood-splattered scenario. What a shocker. Poor Robert.

Dorothy smoothed down her plaid woolen skirt and whispered, "There's more."

More?

"I knew there had to be. Four strangers break in at nighttime, steal nothing and kill only Robert? Why not his Thai wife, too? Or his brother-in-law? No, something was off. My lawyer arranged for a detective to look into it further." She peered birdlike at us over her glasses. "He uncovered a rather salient fact."

"Oh, yes?" Francine managed.

"The man posing as Juliette's brother was actually her lover." Dorothy paused to let that truth bomb land. "Robert triggered the whole sorry mess. The couple pegged him at the airport and played him perfectly over the next three years. As you know, a little bit of flattery worked wonders with that boy," Dorothy scoffed.

"So Robert wasn't sick?" I asked, still floundering.

"Oh, he was quite ill, dear. Juliette's 'special protein powders' did a number on his heart. However, it was a slow process. I suspect my nephew's fatuous self-promotion ultimately spurred the couple to move on to plan B. Murder."

"How positively Machiavellian. They would have gotten away with it, too, if not for you. Robert was blessed to have you in his corner," Francine exclaimed, echoing my thoughts.

Dorothy's blue eyes sparked.

"I did it to get justice for my *sister*. She deserves nothing less."

Francine fell silent. This was a lot to take in.

"It might be hollow comfort, but at least she'll never know the truth," my mother finally managed.

"Exactly. She'd be horrified to think that her actions played a role in the murder of her only child."

"We've sold all of her treasures, Dorothy. There is nothing left."

The octogenarian smiled sadly.

"Please don't fret. I thank you on behalf of my sister for ensuring that they found good homes. Frankly, it's a relief to put the whole unfortunate mess behind me. I'll donate whatever's owing to a charity in her name."

What a horrific ending for Robert. And in his happy place, too. As his aunt and Francine settled up the account, I couldn't help but compare how very different our Thailand was to his. In our experience, everyone couldn't have been kinder or more honest; from Pook, to Anong and Pilat, and certainly the Pepsi and club soda dispensing merchants. I refused to believe that the country was at fault. The sad fact was that Robert could easily have met a similar fate elsewhere. For all his new-found wealth, he couldn't purchase the one thing that would have kept him alive. Street smarts.

Dorothy paused in the doorway and answered the one question we felt we couldn't ask.

"The irony of the whole sorry saga is that Robert never changed his will. He's left everything to me. Juliette gets nothing."

CHAPTER 59

Her Kingdom for a Salesperson

John and I were getting married in seven days. Of the several wedding guests I'd met through FROG, the Kameis traveled the farthest. They flew in from Japan a few days early, and as we met them over drinks at Tolmie, they showered us with gifts, each one symbolic of a long and happy marriage.

"Would it be appropriate to give *them* a little something?" my fiancé wondered as we drove home.

No. The concept of adding yet another item to the still lengthy wedding to-do list was anathema to me.

John gestured toward the back seat awash with presents.

"It's their first visit to Canada's West Coast, Kel. I'm sure they'd appreciate a token."

Fine. Mom could take that on.

After rejecting options from maple syrup to scenic prints, Francine came up with the perfect solution. A pair of Cowichan sweaters. The Indigenous people who create these handknit gems from undyed, handspun sheep's wool, are the Cowichan of Southeastern Vancouver Island. The sweaters are both waterproof and warm, thanks to the high lanolin content. Better yet, their traditional designs such as an eagle, orca or bear speak to their West Coast uniqueness.

When Francine volunteered to zip down to the one department store known for stocking the sweaters, I gratefully accepted. It was a Monday and we weren't busy. However, when she finally staggered back into FROG some four hours later, I was more than a little concerned. What took so long?

She collapsed onto a small but solid blackwood table, her arms wrapped around the huge Hudson's Bay bag.

"Could you drum up some tea, Kel? I'm simply gasping."

There was no point demanding enlightenment. She'd done me a huge favor. We had to follow her playbook.

I returned to find my mother stretched out in a chair, rotating her ankles in tiny circles.

"I'm worn out, Kel. Absolutely worn out."

Dear Lord, she was milking it for all it was worth. Silly me. I should have tackled this job myself. I could have squeezed it in after work.

"Would you believe it took me a good fifteen minutes to even *find* the damn things?"

I now truly regretted not getting myself a coffee.

"No one else was foolish enough to consider buying sweaters. Not in this heat," Francine muttered, flashing a side-eye. "I was all alone and needed help with sizing. But of course, there wasn't a salesperson in sight."

My back molars throbbed and I begged for patience as my mother squeezed her shoulders skyward and slowly lowered them.

"I finally found a sales desk off in the boonies. However, the bored clerk waved me away, implying I'd have better luck wandering about the floor seeking help than hanging about with him. Can you imagine? Honestly their customer service has gone to hell in a handbasket." Francine flicked smug proprietary eyes about her shop. "Well, it took some time, but I *finally* spotted a salesman lounging against a pillar. He was Mr. Kamei's size!"

I smiled and glanced hopefully at the shopping bag. But no. Not yet.

"From the moment Joel slipped on the first sweater, he was a godsend. He zipped it up and pirouetted, enabling me to see the fit from all sides. I was able to reject it outright."

Francine sighed happily.

"He must have tried on at least half a dozen before we finally agreed on an eagle pattern for Mr. Kamei. It spoke to both of us. Mind you, I had to explain how the bird is considered a symbol of great intellect. Joel hadn't a clue."

Francine reached into the bag and produced a thick, caramel-colored cardigan. My heart sang. Blessed with a rolled collar, it boasted a small, chocolate brown and white eagle on either side of the zipper, and a large, regal one on the back. I couldn't think of anything more perfect for the math professor.

"Oooh, someone's been shopping!"

We were so wrapped up in the sweater moment, we hadn't noticed Mrs. Park slip in. Of all people to ignore. I began apologizing profusely but Francine rose above it; yet another perk of being the M.O.B. rather than the bride.

"How lovely to see you, Mrs. Park. Have you got a moment? I've got quite the story about shopping for two of Kelly's wedding guests."

"Yes, you bet, Frankie. I love all things wedding," Mrs. Park enthused, her eyes sparkling.

I held up the heavy sweater as Francine quickly rehashed its selection. With both witnesses now wholly invested, my personal shopper moved on to the selection of Mrs. Kamei's cardigan.

"Joel blossomed under my tutelage. I was about to opt for an orca when the salesman produced the loveliest hummingbird design. While tight on him, it would fit Mrs. Kamei nicely. Unfortunately when he went to take it off, the damn zipper was jammed. Once we finally wrenched it over his head, Joel offered to try and locate an identical one in the same size. Wasn't that thoughtful?"

"Well, that *is* his job, Francine," I exclaimed.

"You'd think so," she smiled mysteriously. "It took him simply ages, Kel. Ages. When he eventually returned, I asked if he'd sourced it out of province."

Mrs. Park giggled with delight and I cracked a smile.

"It's gorgeous. Have a look."

It, too, was utterly perfect. Like Mr. Kamei's, the cardigan had a zipper and rolled collar. A soft gray overall, it also had the same configuration of birds but these ones sported the needle-thin, curved beaks unique to hummingbirds.

"I explained to Joel how the hummingbird is often portrayed as a joyful messenger and represents love, which I think the artistic Mrs. Kamei will appreciate, eh Kel?"

Joyful messages and love? Francine had truly gone above and beyond.

"Oh, she will! Thank you so much, Mom, they're perfect. The Kameis will treasure them forever." My voice caught, causing the women to exchange concerned looks. A lump formed in my throat. God. How embarrassing. If I started crying I wouldn't be able to stop.

"You really should recommend Joel as employee of the month,"

Mrs. Park kindly deflected.

Francine's eyes danced.

"Funny you should say that. You'll never guess what he admitted when I asked him to ring them up."

I dabbed at my nose as both women pretended not to notice.

"The poor man was a tourist, visiting from Edmonton. He was checking out the Vancouver shopping scene before meeting up with his wife at 1."

Mom got a random customer to try on all those sweaters and hunt down even more? Of course she did. I gasped with laughter. Just the perfect tonic for my jangled nerves.

Francine grinned.

"I know, right? What a sport. As thanks, I treated him to soup, a sandwich, and a coffee in the Bay's cafeteria."

Joel's wife was in for a treat. A story of personal shopping and lunch with a complete stranger. The Kameis weren't the only ones who wouldn't soon forget their trip to Vancouver.

CHAPTER 60

I Do! I Do!

I woke at dawn to a symphony of songbirds. It was a relief to just lie there listening, knowing that we weren't going into work today. As much as I loved it, the last thing I wanted to do on my wedding day was peddle product at FROG. Fortunately Francine felt the same.

With Godfrey volunteering to collect the flowers from the florist, and Francine agreeing to stay home to receive gifts, there was nothing left on my "to do" list. I was free to hang out at the hair salon with bridesmaids Ashley and Chelsea, and my honorary bridal party of Wendy and my two besties – Ontario Meems and Kiwi Margaret. I had no plans for the afternoon other than a late lunch at Tolmie.

Wendy's surprise gift of bottles of champagne and orange juice proved a lovely treat at the salon. The morning flew by and the six of us were saying our "see you laters" when Meems pulled me aside for a quiet word.

"I'm up for any last minute jobs, Kel. Seriously. Anything you need."

How kind. While I'd been her maid of honor seven years earlier, she understood my decision to roll with just my eight-year-old nieces Ashley and Chelsea.

"Seriously. I know how hectic it can be just hours before the wedding. I'm happy to pick up film, drop off church flowers, hand out reception maps. Whatever."

Reception maps? We had wedding programs but no maps.

"The UBC Faculty Club might be a bit tricky to find, Kel, if you don't know the campus," she cautioned.

I hadn't thought of that.

We always celebrated special occasions at the Faculty Club when I was younger. Open to UBC faculty members and their guests, kids like Wendy, Mike and I were welcome only in the dining room and the cloak room. However, we did sneak into the vacant "reading room" once to get a closer look at the huge inflatable globe. Always keen to earn my siblings' respect, I plucked it off the stand and began dribbling it down the long corridor. Thankfully, Godfrey caught me before any employees cottoned on to the antics.

My memories of the dining room are of the middle-aged male servers earnestly prepping Caesar salads, and of the round tables dressed with formal white linen tablecloths and heavy silverware. The standards relaxed over time. We stopped going when our friends were hired as bussers and servers. Wishing to avoid the inevitable awkwardness, our family opted for more anonymous celebrations at Vancouver's iconic *Cannery Seafood Restaurant*.

I hadn't been to the Faculty Club since Wendy's wedding reception, some eleven years earlier. She handed out maps. Good Lord. Meems might have a point. I suddenly pictured our hapless guests galloping about the thickly forested University Endowment Lands, searching in vain for the club tucked away in the northern part of the campus.

Okay, we needed a map. However, it was too late to get thick, professional-looking copies printed.

"Your store has a printer, no? How about using it, Kel?"

Meems and I slipped into the shop and sketched an impromptu depiction of the easiest route from the church to the club. Now wasn't the time for perfectionism.

Five sheets in and the machine suddenly jammed. Perhaps upset that we left everything to the last minute, the normally efficient printer spat out just a few more copies before jamming yet again. This recalcitrant effort persisted until the job that should have taken a few minutes, nudged to over an hour. The tiny, windowless room took on the humid aura of a Scandinavian spa, leaving me sorely tempted to ask for a Turkish robe and some soothing mint tea.

"Um, someone's at the door, Kel. Should we hide?" Meems suddenly whispered.

It was too late to ignore the stranger waving from the sidewalk. Damn the printer and its revealing green glow.

"Wow, your stuff is fantastic. I've not been in before. When did you open?" she inquired vacuously.

My customer radar was on high alert. If I didn't shut this visit down immediately, we'd be in for a lengthy spell of rudderless meandering.

"I am sorry, but we're not open. We're closed today," I ventured boldly.

"That kimono looks like it might fit my nephew. What size is it?"

Who knew? I hadn't a clue. My brain was locked in wedding mode.

However, I wasn't the only one at fault here. It's possible that she didn't see the large "Closed Today For Family Celebration" sign plastered on the door. And perhaps she truly didn't hear me just now. But, come on, surely the woman could read the room! Not only were the lights off, but the sales staff didn't act remotely professional. One of us was hiding out in the back room and the other one was a monosyllabic grump. Our casual flip flops, denim cutoffs and wrinkled shirts should have been yet another clue.

I gestured toward my shellacked bridal bouffant and squawked, "Wedding day! I need to rest! GO!"

The visitor slipped out like a startled seal.

Meems and I also fled. Never mind that we were 50 copies short. The guests could carpool.

"Well, all's well that ends well, love," my mother sang out when I finally arrived at Tolmie Street.

Who told her about FROG's latest oblivious newbie?

"Your father forgot the wedding flowers."

Excuse me, what?

"John's mom found them wilting on the backseat of his truck, an hour or so after he picked them up."

Oh my God. He'd never leave Osler in the truck for even five seconds on such a hot day! How could he forget the flowers?

"No, no, it's fine! We threw them in the fridge. They've recovered nicely."

Lost guests and now dead flowers. Honestly, you had to laugh.

"Best get dressed, Kel. Michael will be here soon."

She was referring to the fellow driving us to the church. I'd been friends with Michael for almost 20 years, ever since I crashed our navy blue Volkswagen Beetle during an innocent driving lesson with Godfrey. I lost control while attempting a steep curve on loose gravel. The vehicle shot off the road and onto a rocky embankment, where it orchestrated a series of gymnastic flips akin to the gifted Simone Biles, before finally coming to rest in an elderly couple's tranquil garden. Wheels up. By some miracle,

Godfrey and I escaped without a scratch. Michael's auto body repair shop magically restored the pancaked vehicle to its former glory and we'd been friends and faithful customers ever since.

When he offered to drive me in one of his vintage cars on my wedding day, I was thrilled; more for the chance to be distracted and entertained, than by any vehicle. However, all that changed the instant he pulled into Tolmie's driveway. His vanilla-cream 1936 Rolls Royce Phantom was a bridal treat. As Francine marveled over the plush and roomy interior, I piled into the back behind her, mindful of my dress's fashionably oversized back bow. Godfrey slid in beside me and winked. Things were indeed looking up. We cranked our windows, and my mood lightened to the point that were it any other day, I'd be tempted to ask Michael to just keep driving.

We purred up to the church twenty minutes later. I was relieved to see Christine standing alongside Ashley, Chelsea, and my brother Mike. My fellow runner was a talented seamstress. She'd not only designed and made my pearl-studded midi dress but also generously offered to provide any necessary last minute tweaking.

Michael hopped out and brandished the door open for Francine. My throat closed as she turned to me, her face infused with love.

"You've got a good man there, Kelly, Dad and I know you'll both be very happy," she whispered, her voice catching.

The truth hit me then with the full force of a tossed bridal bouquet. I was marrying John today.

"Thank you, Mom and thank you, Dad. For everything," I squeaked, grateful for the waterproof mascara.

"You look gorgeous, Kel. Our very best wishes to you and John. Okay, come on Mom, let's get this wedding underway," my brother kindly redirected.

Francine and I exchanged a pair of wobbly grins and she tucked

NEVER, NEVER, HARDLY EVER

her hand in Mike's elbow.

"It's not too late to change your mind, Kelly," our chauffeur joked, jangling his keys as Christine smoothed down my dress and fluffed out its bow. Classic Michael with his perfect timing. I giggled and the rest joined in.

"It's a go, then. Good. I'll be waiting for you and your husband right here." Michael beamed and scooted inside with Christine.

Francine and I exchanged one last smile before my brother led her into the church.

There were now just four of us outside.

The girls smiled shyly.

"Well, this is rather pleasant," Godfrey teased.

It was.

"I suppose we'd better find John. He'll be wondering where we are, Dad."

My father grinned and offered me his elbow.

It was unbearably hot inside the church. I spied a lucky few fanning themselves with reception maps. As the organ soared, the girls glanced at me for confirmation, and began to make their way slowly down the aisle. This was their first wedding and they were acting like seasoned veterans.

Godfrey squeezed my hand and tucked it into his arm. As the attention now fell upon the two of us, I focused on my groom. John's Scottish ancestors would be most proud. He was kitted out in a woolen kilt sporting the dark green, black, navy blue, red and white colors of the Mackenzie tartan. His eyes sparkled and the silver buttons on his black woolen jacket gleamed. He appeared confident and at ease. This outfit wasn't a wedding one-off. A gifted Highland dancer, John had been wearing kilts since he was wee.

"You made it," John teased as I took my place beside him.

We pivoted toward the Reverend and the world shrank. The incessant flapping, random coughs and the overbearing heat faded away, leaving just the three of us in a nuptial cocoon. As we exchanged our vows, I suddenly remembered how I felt when John met me at the ferry on Paula's wedding day. He and I were indeed blessed to have found one another. We locked eyes and I understood that he knew it, too.

CHAPTER 61

Scam or Heartbreak?

The honeymoon was definitely over. Six months on and I could not be happier to escape our home. My father-in-law, the professional contractor, performed a thorough assessment of our new house and discovered that at least two-thirds of the foundation's drain tiles needed to be replaced. Immediately. The bungalow was currently mud pit central. The deep open trench and piles of dirt were a soupy mess, thanks to last night's torrential downpour.

That delight paled into insignificance, however, once I got to work. Overnight, FROG had morphed into a seedy pub. It reeked of beer and stale cigarettes. Francine's abrupt greeting only fueled my concerns.

"Kelly, I won't take no for an answer."

I froze in the doorway.

"Robert Kelly needs $500 cash. Immediately," she explained, pointing to the stranger.

Mr. Kelly, blessed with shoulder-length matted hair, grubby jeans and greasy sweatshirt, suddenly tipped sideways in his chair.

As Francine began awkwardly rubbing his back, it was official. We'd crossed over into the twilight zone. I stole closer to ascertain his level of consciousness. The slack face and droopy eyelids, while impressive, confirmed my suspicions. The man was soused.

"Francine, may I have a word with you in the office, please?" I asked, desperate for some insight.

My mother gently steered her charge onto the platform's carpeted stairs.

"Excuse me, Robert. I won't be a minute," she whispered as if to a sick infant.

"What the hell, Mom. What's going on? Who is he?"

Francine's face crumpled.

"Things couldn't be worse. Robert is so upset he can't even speak. I had to call his Uncle Landry to get the details." She pulled me further into the office and lowered her voice.

"Robert and his wife are from Vancouver Island. They were involved in a dreadful crash in Chilliwack yesterday. Their car burst into flames! Robert got out safely but his pregnant wife is clinging to life in the hospital. She could be paralyzed. We have to help. He doesn't even have the taxi fare to visit her." Her eyes filled with tears.

How horrible. It must be all over the news ... Wait. What? There wasn't a peep about this anywhere. Not in the newspaper, on television or on the radio.

"Mom, hang on a sec. Let's think about this carefully."

Francine held up her hand.

"Kelly, I *have* thought about it. A fellow human has reached out to me for help. I will help."

"But, Mom. What if it's not true?"

The steely resolve crept back into her face.

"How could you even *ask* that, Kelly?"

"I'm sorry, Mom, but why isn't this headline news?"

"Christ, I don't know! Maybe it happened on a logging road, or maybe it involved just their car, or maybe it only made the local Chilliwack paper. I don't know nor care."

Francine had well and truly drunk the Kool Aid.

"Okay, let's say it did happen. Why us? Why can't Uncle Landry cough up the cash?"

"Uncle Landry doesn't live here, Kelly. He lives miles away. Up north," Francine explained, speaking as if I was addled. "He was using a ship-to-shore radio from his fishing boat. It was very difficult to understand him. He kept cutting in and out." She shook her head sadly. "The Kellys have no friends or family here in the Lower Mainland. Thankfully Uncle Landry remembered 'the kind antique dealers with the lovely pink cloisonné vase in the window.'" She glanced back toward the silent showroom. "Robert needs me. You go and withdraw the money. And don't fuss. Uncle Landry will pay us back. He's flying down tomorrow."

How fortuitous that the "lovely pink cloisonné vase" happened to be in the window.

"Mom, I can't recall chatting with *anyone* about that vase, least of all some random dude. Can you?"

Francine stiffened, her lips forming a sour, thin line.

"For God's sake have some compassion!" she spat, showering me with a thin film of saliva. "Look at that poor man! He can't even sit up."

I wiped my face with my sleeve and peeked out through the *noren*. Mr. Kelly was now doubled over, his head flopped onto his knees.

"Mom, listen. I don't feel good about this. Something's not right."

"I could *not* be more disappointed, Kelly. I don't think I really know you."

The frigid message seared my soul. Christ. I had to concede, if only a little.

"Okay. Look, $500 is excessive. Let's give him $150. It's enough to get a cab, a cheap room and a bite to eat. If it's a scam, that's a much kinder hit to us than $500."

"Fine. I do wish you'd be more charitable, but I can see it's not in you, Kelly." She swept out, leaving my calculating heart properly crushed. I'd really done it this time. This wasn't our usual bickering over the acquisition of some Asian artifact. This was deeply personal. I'd failed Francine as her daughter.

"Robert, my bookkeeper has agreed to release only $150. In light of that diminished amount, I insist on reserving a room for you tonight at the Burrard Motor Inn. It's central, comfortable and where my brother stays when he's in town." She glanced back at me before adding, "I'll personally pay for it."

I perked up. Here we go. The ultimate litmus test. Would Mr. Kelly request accommodation closer to his wife? Or would he elect to stay downtown?

Clearly struggling to focus, he tilted his head and blinked at Francine.

"Thanksh. But could ya make it the Balmoral?"

Mic drop.

His preferred hotel was 60 miles from Chilliwack. It was also notorious for its huge beer parlor.

"Nonsense, Robert. I can't let you stay there. You need pampering. Please let me do that for you," she stubbornly insisted. The fellow drew in his shoulders and stared at his boots.

Unbelievable. My mother still held the faith. Fine. I'd withdraw her precious $150. It was her shop, her money.

I stalked back from the bank to find Robert splayed across a fine example of a Chinese nineteenth century blackwood chair, looking disarmingly innocent with his head lolled backwards and his neck exposed. Francine bustled forward with the efficiency of a neonatal care nurse.

"Could you please drop him at the hotel when he wakes up? I've got the movie people coming in and I don't want to miss them."

What a delightful concept – 15 minutes locked up in my car with a suspected charlatan. I couldn't wait.

As I thrust the envelope at Francine, it acted like smelling salts. Mr. Kelly came to with a snort.

"Everything is arranged at the Burrard Motor Inn, Robert. Kelly will escort you there. You've enough cash to get a good meal, a hot shower and transportation to the hospital," my mother cooed.

He struggled to his feet and pocketed the envelope without looking inside.

"Thank you, Jackie. Blesh you."

"I just wish I could do more, Robert," she murmured, glaring in my direction. "All the very best to you and your family."

Francine embraced him in a heartfelt hug and reluctantly released him to my care.

As we entered the underground parking lot, Robert suddenly lurched and grabbed my wrist.

"It'd be better if you took me to the Balmoral, Shelley. Uncle Landry's friend is there. He'll give me more money."

He took no notice of my incredulous stare.

"I'll hit up Jackie's hotel after that. She's a good woman, your boss. A good woman." He hiccuped and patted his bulging side pocket.

As we settled into my hatchback, I cranked the windows and pondered my role. Was I supposed to wait for him at the Balmoral? Or should I just drop him and dash? Robert was no help. He simply closed his eyes and belched. We drove the entire way in silence. "Thanksh. 'Bye," Robert mumbled when I pulled up to the Balmoral. As he staggered toward the building, I took note of the two entrances, "Lobby" and "Pub." I sped off when he selected the latter.

Francine wasn't happy.

"I hate to think of Robert coming out to find you gone. What if he can't remember which hotel I booked? I mean, he really was struggling to hold it together." Anticipating more negativity, Francine held up her hand. "No. I want you to just do this one thing for me. Okay?" I nodded. "Imagine being in a strange city, John is at death's door in some random hospital and you're all alone without any money. What would you do?"

"I'd accompany him in the ambulance and get the social worker to call my family from the hospital, Mom."

It was a good thing there was only an hour left of work.

Sleep evaded me that night. I kept thinking about our different reactions to Mr. Kelly's situation. Was my response one of simple street smarts or was I jealous and resentful of Francine's steadfast generosity to a complete stranger? Would I have reacted differently if she wasn't my mother? I hadn't a clue, even though we'd been working together for over seven years now. Mother/daughter dynamics were complicated, toss in a working relationship and the waters got very muddied indeed.

I called Francine at 6 a.m. the next morning, just before Osler's walk.

"I owe you an apology, Mom. I'm sorry for yesterday. You were very kind to poor Robert."

"Aw, Kel, I knew you'd come around eventually. Thank you. We'll get the latest from Uncle Landry when he drops by today. Hopefully he's got good news. Enjoy your day off."

I reached out again in the afternoon.

"Nothing yet, Kel," Francine admitted. "I'll call you as soon as I hear anything."

Mom's voice was oddly subdued when she called just after 6 p.m.

"Robert never checked into the Burrard Motor Inn, Kelly," she whispered.

"And Uncle Landry?" I ventured to ask.

"A no-show as well."

Not good.

"There's more."

I could barely make out what she was saying.

"Mrs. Kelly isn't a patient at the Chilliwack hospital."

"Maybe she goes by a different last name, Mom," I suggested, gently. She didn't need sarcasm now. That would be adding iodine to the open wound.

"No pregnant accident victim was admitted. They told me all Chilliwack trauma patients are sent to the Royal Columbian hospital in New Westminster. I called them and she's not there. They suggested I reach out to the Vancouver General and St. Paul's hospitals. Negative on all counts."

She confessed to feeling both foolish and betrayed.

"Well, let's focus on the positive, Mom. You could have insisted on paying the full $500."

"Yes, we did manage to safeguard $350 and I didn't have to pay for the hotel room. That's something, isn't it? However, we're meant to be taking in money, not doling it out."

"I love you, Mom," I replied and gently hung up. There was nothing more to say.

As the days floated by with continued radio silence from the car-crash gang, Francine called the Vancouver Police Fraud Detail.

It didn't go well.

"How demoralizing, Kel. The detective had two pieces of advice. One, I should consider the money as a $150 voluntary contribution, and two, I should rewatch *The Sting* to get a few pointers on how to prevent it from happening again."

She didn't need *The Sting*, she had me.

My ears perked up when a certain news bulletin popped up on my car radio some three weeks later.

"Dozens of merchants from Kamloops to Victoria and Vancouver have apparently been taken in by the couple. The 'victim' claims to have been in an accident and is too upset to reveal more. The merchant calls a 'relative' who shares the tragic details of the victim's pregnant wife clinging to life in the hospital. Recalling a specific connection with the store, he requests some cash to temporarily help his loved ones out. The scam is revealed when the promises of reimbursement go unfulfilled …"

So Francine wasn't the only one taken in. That would soften the blow. I couldn't wait to tell her.

CHAPTER 62

Wired

I was concerned about Francine's mental state two weeks on from the Robert Kelly chicanery. A gloomy pall settled over her that no amount of cheery customer chats or jocular "Who am I?" games could dispel.

But everything changed the day she and her friend Barb, the elementary school teacher, met for lunch.

"We've cooked up a wonderful plan, Kel!" Francine squealed upon their return.

I braced for the revelation.

"We'll soon be selling my papier-maché creatures and life-size wire figures!"

I suspected they'd opted for wine with lunch.

"We were chatting about how popular our Thai papier-maché pieces are, and Barb mentioned she makes adorable papier-maché bunnies every Easter with her fifth-grade students. I suddenly realized I could make them! Just think of the savings, Kel. Barb's agreed to teach me how to make the bunnies and I'll expand the line with pigs, chickens, cats, etc. The possibilities are endless.

I'm so excited!"

Welcome back, Madame Wasabi.

"We moved on to other things I could make and sell. You know how I adore Sherry Grauer's marvelous life-size wire sculptures?" My mother beamed as I struggled to catch up. "You love the idea of them, too, don't you, Barb?"

"Oh, I do. The hollow figures sound so life-like. I think they'll do very well in the shop."

"Exactly. I'm sure I can figure out how to make them. How hard can it be?"

I thought back to our conversation with Sherry Grauer, the inspiring British Columbian artist behind the life-sized human wire figures. She said even though she wore thick gloves, the wire gave her blisters. She had to take a break between each creation. Knowing how Francine struggled with the odd sliver, I couldn't imagine her coping with one painful pustule, let alone several. However, now wasn't the time to mention it. My mother needed to dream.

In true Madame Wasabi fashion, things kicked off quickly. She and Barb created dozens of fortune teller-sized papier-maché orbs the next weekend. Francine assured Godfrey that the storage in the backyard shed was temporary. The blobs would soon be transformed into "unique and quirky creatures the likes of which Vancouver has never seen before."

I appreciated the transformational impact on my boss. Madame Wasabi lingered. She chatted up the impending new lines with FROG visitors, Mrs. King, and random patrons at The Granville Diner. Everyone thought they sounded brilliant, especially the youthful stranger sporting a colorful quilted patchwork vest.

"What vision, Frankie! Those wire figures sound amazing! But where do you create? Surely not here ..." he exclaimed, gesturing about the shop.

"What an amusing thought. No, I have access to a charming cottage in West Point Grey."

I smirked at the optics of an idyllic wisteria-draped hobbit-like dwelling. He'd be shocked by the reality of Tolmie Street's humble shed.

"Wow. Lucky you. I couldn't work squirreled away. I need the presence of other creatives." The fellow fanned out his colorful vest and pirouetted. "What do you think of my latest effort?"

"Oh, you *are* gifted," Francine purred, studying the tiny stitches.

"Do you think so? How kind. Thank you, Frankie." The artist squinted and cocked his head. "You know, I think you'd do well in our downtown art loft. You should come check it out."

Downtown art loft. Francine's face lit up hearing these three innocent words. She was smitten and requested an impromptu viewing. The old alarm bells jangled. This new venture was getting a bit too real. Papier-mâché balls were one thing, additional rent payments were quite another. I prayed the space wouldn't be suitable.

"The place just *oozes* inspiration, Kel. *Everyone* is a creative. Painters, sculptures, potters, you name it, they're there. I've got a whole new group of friends to draw from. I can't wait for you to meet them," Francine enthused, her eyes sparkling. "My unit is tiny but I can put in shelving. Isn't it thrilling?"

No, it was *chilling*.

Madame Wasabi continued to shower her plans about like fairy dust, with Doris being her latest victim.

"Wow. You're amazing, Frankie. I can't picture the wire figures, but I've always adored the cute papier-mâché creatures you bring in from Thailand!" she marveled.

"Yes! Mine will be *just* like them, and with no need to cover the costs of shipping or Customs' fees, they'll be even more reasonably priced!"

"Put me down for a dozen. No, two dozen!"

"You are a dear."

"Well, I just know that these new lines are going to take off. You're unstoppable. I think you should consider the possibility of establishing a chain of Frankie Robinson's!"

"Do you think so? It would be a huge undertaking, dear."

Doris shook her head.

"You could start small, Frankie. Your son lives in Calgary. He could vet the space and hire the employees. How fun! You could open in Toronto next, then Montreal ..."

Francine looked over at me and winked. It was heartwarming to see her so happy.

I wasn't surprised though, when in true Madame Wasabi fashion, she soon switched allegiances, opting to focus on the wire sculptures.

"The papier-maché balls can wait, Kel. I just have to make the ears, beaks and wings. With Barb's help, they'll be a breeze. I've never worked with wire, though, and you know how I love a challenge."

We got our first glimpse of the coiled wire when it was delivered to FROG by mistake. The medium looked very unforgiving and I remarked on how similar it was to the cattle fencing at the farm.

"It's nothing like it," Francine declared with a sniff.

It was a struggle to heft it into her beloved 20-year-old, sky blue Mercedes sedan. Relieved that Bill, patchwork quilt man, was standing by to help her unload on the other end, I didn't give my mother another thought until she reappeared shortly before closing.

"Kelly, thank God you're still here. I need to sit. I've got a splitting headache," Francine managed before crumpling onto a nearby stool.

I felt the first stirrings of alarm. A splitting headache and the demise of Madame Wasabi were inexorably linked. Yet, we were only on day one of the glorious art studio experiment. As much as I ached to learn the truth, I didn't push it but dashed out for a restorative treat from The Granville Diner.

Francine eventually recovered enough to speak.

"It's dreadful, just dreadful."

I nibbled at my cranberry orange scone.

"You've no idea what I've been through, Kelly."

She favored me with tormented eyes.

"The day began so innocently. When I discovered the wire spool was held together by another wire wrapping, I thought I could simply find the wrapping's two ends and pry them apart. But I couldn't see properly. The lighting was too poor."

I made a mental note of the need for extra lighting fixtures and brighter bulbs.

"I dragged the coil out into the brightly lit corridor. That's when everything went to hell in a handbasket. Christ, Kel!"

She had my full attention now.

"When I pried the ends apart the freed coil took on a life of its own! It lashed about the corridor, thrashing this way and that. The noise was horrific. The metallic whipping went on forever. It was as if I was conjuring a never-ending thunderclap. Folks *streamed* out of their units. When it finally ceased thrashing about we couldn't hear a thing. Not a thing. I only just got my hearing back." She frowned. "Don't laugh, Kelly. It was damn humiliating."

"I'm sorry, but picturing you struggling to maintain a semblance of dignity as the wire whips all around you is downright hysterical. It's just so typical," I gasped.

Francine smiled.

"Yes, well. We were all shell-shocked, I can tell you. I don't know how I found the strength to motion for help."

"That must have been interesting."

She flashed a side eye.

"That's putting it mildly. The wire is so damn stiff and unforgiving, it took four of us to scoop up the gnarly mess. When we finally tossed it into my little cubby and slammed the door, you could hear it thrashing about again, like some trapped wild animal."

Her mood suddenly shifted.

"I don't know if I can go back, Kelly."

What a sobering and raw admission from our indomitable gal.

"Mom, I think that at almost 70, you've earned the right to be kind to yourself," I decreed slowly.

"Yes, thank you, Kel. I don't need the hassle do I? We've got plenty to do right here."

"But what about the lease, Mom? Can you get out of it?"

She choked on the last of her scone.

"Oh God, the lease. How do I get out of the damn lease?" she asked, spewing crumbs down the front of her dress. As she continued to cough, I got a flash of brilliance.

"Your asthma! You could say that it's been triggered by the combination of the artists' different chemicals and you're worried about your health going forward."

Francine lunged for the phone.

"Hello, Bill? It's Frankie Robinson. Pardon? *Frankie!* I'm sorry, no, I can't speak any louder. I'm finding it difficult to breathe. I'm just off to the doctor. Excuse me." She coughed deeply into the receiver. "Pardon? Yes, it was *quite* the afternoon. Hang on."

She unleashed a series of alarming hacks and wheezes.

"Sorry about that, Bill. Yes, my lungs are acting up. I fear I'm going to have to cancel my lease. I had scarlet fever as a child and the slightest thing can set them off. It's the soupy mix of different chemicals in the loft, you see. If this is the reaction after just one day, I can't imagine what a steady immersion would be like. It'd probably do me in. I'm *absolutely* devastated."

And the Oscar goes to ...

CHAPTER 63

Gracious Acceptance

F rancine was on a work holiday in Honolulu when our friend swung in on a Saturday. Julia smiled when I admired the red highlights of her brunette wig.

"Thank you, Kelly. Good Morning. I need your help with something today, if you don't mind."

"Of course. How can I help?"

"Now that I'm down to my final weeks ..."

Excuse me, what?

"... I have just one thing left to do."

My throat closed as Julia began ticking off points on her fingers like a grocery list.

"The bathroom's renovated. My clothing is donated. I've shipped my good jewelry to my sister in Germany. I've given the costume bits to my goddaughter who lives here. I've said goodbye to my dearest friends. There's just one more thing left to do and I'd appreciate your help with it."

I didn't want to hear any more. It took every ounce of willpower not to bolt out into the street.

Julia surged ahead like the tide.

"I'm here to choose my memorial headstone."

Oh, come on. It was way too early for that. All the medical bulletins were positive. Julia's doctor confirmed her health was stable just two months ago. He advised her to keep doing whatever she was doing. She'd also been interviewed recently on the radio regarding her stellar attitude toward cancer. And only last week, Julia bought some colorful Chinese watercolors for the bathroom. It was a normal visit. Granted she'd gotten emotional over Francine's impulsive gift of a small Japanese lacquer box, but who wouldn't? Julia was beating cancer. She *was*.

"Will you help me choose it, Kelly?"

No! I wasn't equipped to help select something as personal as a memorial headstone! I wasn't nearly emotionally mature enough for that. We needed Francine and we needed her *right* now. But, she was thousands of miles away. Dear God. It would have to be me.

I dug deep, deeper than I'd ever done before at FROG. However, the brutal truth was too much. This act was so real, so *final*. A memorial headstone was something that family and friends would visit to *remember* her by.

Julia swept me into a hug as I began to weep.

"Hush, hush. I *know* it's a huge ask, Kelly. I do. Please understand that I find it comforting. I can't leave it to David. You know he'd opt for something plastic and gaudily inappropriate."

That ridiculous observation about her husband made me giggle. David had exquisite taste. She gently released me and began to slowly weave throughout the crowded store. I started crying again. I couldn't help it. Julia was eyeing each bronze Buddha, ivory carving and wooden plaque as if she was selecting a wedding present for a special couple.

"What can you tell me about this piece, Kelly?" she asked, pointing to a recent acquisition.

Nothing. I didn't want to tell her anything about the ancient Japanese gray stone carving which stood a foot-and-a-half high and was four-inches thick. However, as she continued to smile warmly, I forced myself to reply.

"It weighs a ton," I managed.

Get a grip, Kelly. If she can do this, so can you. I blew into a tissue, took a deep breath and began again. This time in a stronger voice.

"It's over 200 years old. It's a carving of Dosojin, the Japanese guardians who protect travelers, villagers, and folks in transition, from epidemics and evil spirits."

Julia listened, her head cocked to one side. As she slowly circled the piece, I stood back, dearly hoping I'd suddenly wake up to a carefree sunny morning, in my own bed next to John.

"I like the idea of something protecting me for eternity," Julia exclaimed before nodding decisively. "Yes! It's perfect. I'll take it."

Not a bad dream, then.

A living nightmare.

When I dashed into the office on the pretext of acquiring some bubble wrap, the room was spinning. I grabbed onto the bathroom door and breathed. I could hear her humming softly to herself. I channeled some of that courage and snatched up the wrap and a roll of tape, and strode back into the showroom.

Nevermind that the carving had survived centuries of extreme weather exposure. This puppy was getting the royal treatment. I swaddled it in countless layers of bubble wrap and reams of packing tape. However, my heart lurched when we viewed the finished product. I'd somehow created an entombed chubby toddler. Christ.

"I'll heft it out to the car for you, Julia. But what about on the other end? How will you get it inside?" I blathered.

Julia shook her head and grinned.

"Let's just hope I don't get pulled over on the way home, Kelly. It'd stir up a lot of questions."

I was still laughing when I gingerly lowered it onto the backseat of her car where nothing short of a powerful earthquake could dislodge it. We shared yet another giggle as Julia insisted on buckling it into a seatbelt.

"Thank you, Kelly, for everything."

She hugged me and drove off.

I was overwhelmed with guilt. I'd behaved so poorly; I hated crying in front of people. Lord knows I always distracted myself in darkened movie theaters by making up silly words composed from the "exit" sign. Yet, today, when it *really* mattered, I unraveled like a cheap sock. Julia tolerated those shameful tears so well. I hoped I hadn't ruined the experience for her, that it wasn't too trying. And what was with that excessive wrap job? I prayed she didn't think it disrespectful, that I was playing the fool.

When I thought about her gracious acceptance of death, I suddenly remembered the unfortunate Robert Sheldon. He hadn't the remotest notion that he was about to die. Was knowing better?

When Julia slipped in again just before closing time, I was shattered. I barely noticed her placing something onto the nearest tansu. I just knew she had second thoughts which meant we'd have to go through the entire exercise all over again.

"I am so sorry for upsetting you earlier, Kelly."

My pulse raced as I realized she was struggling not to cry.

"Julia, please ..."

"No, let me finish, Kelly."

I nodded, my throat closing yet again.

"I couldn't have managed today without your help. Not at all.

Thank you, Kelly."

I gasped as a tear slipped down her cheek.

"I'm so sorry I upset you. So very sorry." Julia's voice broke and time stopped. Neither of us spoke until she gathered herself. "Please accept this gift as a small token of my *deep* appreciation, Kelly, for your help today and for always." Hugging me quickly, she whispered a soft "Goodbye, dear friend," and fled.

Her gift broke me. Utterly. This selfless soul not only thought to console me with *two* dozen roses, but also somehow managed to remember that Kelly McKenzie preferred yellow over red.

I never saw the remarkable Julia Jones again. As per her wishes, David phoned us when she entered palliative care four months later. She passed away the next day.

As with everything, Julia planned her memorial to perfection.

Realizing it could take a while for the over one thousand mourners to file into the historic church, she hired an elegant string quartet to serenade those waiting outside. When Francine and I squeezed into a crowded pew at the back, I managed to hold it together until I recognized the gleaming blue and white urn containing Julia's ashes. She'd purchased it from FROG two years earlier.

A lump lodged in my throat as I realized she'd deliberately kept its true purpose a secret.

"Oh, Kel, look at the flowers," my mother murmured.

Five stunning orchids, each one tall and curving gently in their sang-de-boeuf pots, provided the perfect cheerful yellow backdrop for the urn.

The memorial was just under an hour. David stole the show with a loving and humorous tribute to his late wife. The entire congregation burst out laughing when he admitted that Julia insisted on editing the final copy. Of course, she did.

As we left the church, I offered up a silent acknowledgment of the successful completion of her final list.

But Julia had one more item left to tick.

We couldn't believe it when a courier dropped by FROG the next morning with a very special present.

Mom's voice trembled as she read out the attached note.

"Julia wanted to especially thank you for the love that you always extended to her, as do I. Thank you, Frankie and Kelly. Be well. Sincerely, David."

What an honor. Out of her hundreds of friends, Julia had chosen us, the FROG shopkeepers, as recipients of one of the five magnificent orchids in the sang-de-boeuf pots. The symbolism didn't escape us. As we learned on that orchid tour with Ole in Thailand, yellow orchids represent friendship and new beginnings.

Thank you, dear friend. You will be missed.

CHAPTER 64

Christmas Epiphanies

If ever Francine and I needed a pick-me-up, it was now. We agreed it was time to let in the light and banish not only our sadness over Julia's passing but also the lingering distrust caused by Mr. Kelly and his Uncle Landry. With yet another shipment to debut, we opted for an early Christmas party complete with tasty festive treats like boozy eggnog, buttery shortbread and spicy mincemeat tarts, along with the usual bottomless wine for 150 of our best FROG friends.

Over three decades later, I marvel how Francine and I managed to crack open a shipment, rearrange the entire shop *and* host a party, all within two days. Then again, there were multiple examples of equivalent effort. The initial one, of course, being that of the ceiling flood crisis some seven years earlier.

The boss and I got off to an early start this December morning, slapping up privacy newspapers on the door and windows, as well as a large note announcing FROG's closure for the day. Meanwhile, Bert and his current flunky Arthur were out in the hallway, unloading the uncrated shipment from Tolmie Street.

They were well stuck in; the jettisoned brown paper, Styrofoam and cardboard made navigating the narrow back passageway rather interesting.

The two men earned their hefty tip over the next three hours. They cheerfully shifted the heavier pieces into position in the showroom and hauled away the trash. Once they left, we downed a modest lunch of cottage cheese and rye crisps in anticipation of the evening's hefty caloric intake.

Francine and I were contemplating the all-important window display when someone suddenly rapped on the papered-over door. I rolled my eyes as she clamped a finger to her lips. Of course I understood we couldn't entertain a soul, not with the hours of work still ahead.

When the knocking persisted, I feared it could be a second visit from my wedding day gal. But the verbal assault veered from her playbook. Piercing shrieks of "Cooee! Frankie Robinson!" ripped through the door's metal mailbox slot, leaving my teeth throbbing as if chomping on tinfoil.

Francine held on admirably before finally caving. I winced as she gingerly peeled back a tiny scrap of newspaper on the premise that it could be Billie. Of course it wasn't. She could no more bellow like an Australian sheepherder than sprint down the street.

"It's Mrs. Edmundson, Kel," Francine whispered.

No, not today of all days. The West Vancouver septuagenarian was one of FROG's staunchest looky-loos. Yet to actually purchase anything, she had a fondness for treating the shop as her private art gallery while "just killing time between appointments."

"Get back here, Mom. Now!" I hissed as if to a dog.

Francine slowly backed away from the door.

"Cooee! Frankie! I saw the newspaper move!"

"Christ! What nonsense. I'll put a stop to it, Kel."

Francine unlocked the door and barked through an inch wide opening, "We're closed all day!"

The unwelcome visitor refused to listen. Wielding sharp elbows, she squeezed inside. Mrs Edmundson couldn't quite hide her distaste of our sartorial elegance. My grubby torn T-shirt and Francine's faded, once-loved sweatshirt with its prancing fawn earned a scornful gasp.

"My doctor's appointment isn't for another 20 minutes. Ooh, Frankie, you've been shopping. You girls must have *so* much fun on your buying trips!" Mrs. Edmundson burbled, spinning about joyfully.

Yet another person incapable of reading a room.

"I can't have this. You need to stop it, right now."

Mrs. Edmundson flinched.

"Look around you. Have you ever seen such chaos here? Have you?"

Go Mom!

The startled visitor could only splutter.

"No, I thought not. We're hosting a *huge* gala tonight. That's why it looks as if a bomb exploded. The gallery is *not* open." Francine paused to let that zinger sink in, before skating on as if wrapping up a Fine Arts 101 lecture. "Thank you for your interest, dear. Now if you don't mind, I'll see you to the door."

The woman found herself out on the sidewalk before she could blink.

"Jesus. I won't be making that mistake again anytime soon, Kel, not for love or money," Francine assured me with a rueful grin.

Just one more story to add to our cast of memorable characters, Mom.

After a concentrated push worthy of a military effort, we managed to have FROG positively transformed by 4:30. She was now inviting, elegant and ready to party.

I couldn't believe the jolly knot of folks hovering outside before the official opening time.

"We thought you could use some help with last minute touch ups, Kelly," Ed chortled, as Beth, Susan, Evelyn and Noah grinned alongside. "We hope you don't mind!"

How very thoughtful.

The skies opened just after 7. Wet wool and damp leather became the prevailing odor, and you couldn't see through the fogged window. However, it didn't matter. With a turnout of well over eighty percent, the shop was humming with chatty and excited guests. Francine and I were thrilled.

I was about to check on Billie when someone tugged on my sleeve, leaving me scrambling for a name. Harold Smith. He'd not been in since purchasing the Thai wooden ibexes, a good three years earlier.

"How are you, Harold?"

Distracted, he took his time answering.

"Oh sorry. I'm fine. I'm just looking for my mom. She tagged along with Seamus and me tonight and I can't wait to introduce you."

I panicked, trying to recall a random snippet concerning his mother.

"Ah, there she is."

As the woman emerged from the crowd, I relaxed. I knew her. Slender as a bookmark and sporting a stunning necklace strung with colorful beads the size of boulders, she stared at me, too. We'd met before. But when? Where?

"Kelly, this is my mother, Elsbeth Smith. Mom, this is Kelly Robinson."

"We bought your house! I'm a McKenzie now," I squawked.

"Pardon, dear?"

"My husband and I bought your house. John McKenzie and I bought your house!"

Elsbeth and Seamus broke into surprised smiles while Harold turned the color of putty.

"Of course!" Elsbeth twittered before turning to Seamus and her visibly shaken son. "Remember?"

"Yes! You went with the young couple, even though they presented the lowest offer of the three, right?" Seamus exclaimed, looking for confirmation from his partner.

Harold only had eyes for me.

"Oh God. I am SO sorry, Kelly."

Poor Harold was remembering the state of the basement. It was raining on move-in day. The water-based paint on the concrete floor quickly turned to liquid, thanks to that problem with the drain tiles. The movers tracked the crimson goo throughout the house, transforming it into a crime scene.The only thing missing was a corpse.

The horrors didn't stop there.

The basement's bookshelf also offered up a unique treat. The wall of sagging particle boards contained dozens of moldy books. It would be months before anyone with allergies could safely pop downstairs.

"Honestly, if I'd known *you* had bought it ...," Harold spluttered.

I ached to put the fellow at ease. Kind enough to show up tonight, Harold needn't know that John and I spent days peeling away the sodden books and tossing them along with the shelves. Or that the tip of my left big toe was permanently numb from the endless kneeling required to scrape off the floor goo.

"Please, Harold. You mustn't worry about a thing. Truly, "

"You sound *just* like your mother, Kelly," he noted. "She'd say something kind like that."

Interesting. I'd been hearing that a lot of late.

"John and I love the house. You did a wonderful remodel of the upstairs. The brass light fixtures and fireplace screen are new, are they not?"

"Yes, they were all Harold's idea." Elsbeth beamed proudly, oblivious to her son's discomfort.

My thoughts wandered. I had to tell John about this bizarre coincidence.

However, Harold remained fixated.

"After donating and trashing *so* much stuff, Kelly, we ran out of steam when it came to the basement. We left you with a horrible mess. I'm so sorry."

I suddenly recalled Harold's comments about growing up with three siblings and a mother who kept *everything*. Jesus. Elsbeth lived there for 34 years. The prep leading to our possession day must have been exhausting. You couldn't fault them for abandoning the effort.

"I don't think we've seen you since you popped by our place!" Seamus blurted, desperate to divert Harold's attention.

It didn't help. As I recalled their glossy West End apartment, Harold and I locked eyes, both of us visualizing the differences between it and our dank cellar. The poor guy. What were the chances that the house he grew up in would be bought by someone from his carefully constructed new life?

"How embarrassing, Kelly. I'm poleaxed ..."

Enough. With his distress teetering toward Harry Potter's self-chastising Dobby, we needed a reboot. And a drink. John could wait. I eased into the crowd. After chatting to Billie, sharing the provenance of a Korean document chest with one couple, placing a hold on a Chinese altar table for another, and writing up a sales slip for a Tibetan lamp, I finally made it to the makeshift bar.

I ordered two white wines and took a moment to absorb the extraordinary coincidence. You couldn't make this stuff up. John had to meet them. He'd never believe me otherwise. Nor would Francine.

I caught a glimpse of my mother's Thai silk mauve dress through the crowd, and sidled over.

"Hi, Kelly. You remember the McPhersons."

I smiled warmly at the young couple, certain we'd never met.

"Now, Mr. and Mrs. McPherson, as always, you're welcome to pay for the kaidan-dansu on the Never, Never, Hardly Ever plan. I'll give you a moment to think about it. I'll just have a quick word with my daughter."

We slipped a few feet away.

"I think it's going rather well, don't you?" Francine asked.

"Yes, I'm glad we went for it, Mom."

"Me, too, Kel. Me, too."

Her face awash with emotion, I knew exactly what she was thinking. Julia's nod to new beginnings was indeed the way forward.

"I should get back to the McPhersons." Francine said, glancing around the crowded room. She tilted her head slightly to the left. "Gerome and Dan are over there, pouring over the funa-dansu (sea chest). Can you go and talk to them, Kel?"

Yes.

But first, a wee detour to my husband and Godfrey. Both were chatting easily with the couple who purchased the last of our lush, sequined Thai elephant hangings.

Apologizing for the interruption, I grabbed John's elbow and whispered, "Can you run this wine to Harold, please? He's in the gray sweater, standing over there with his mom Elsbeth and his partner Seamus."

"Elsbeth looks familiar, Kel. Who is she?"

"Oh, just wait. All will become clear once you share that you're my husband. Trust me," I smiled. "But, whatever you do, *do not* mention our basement."

John flashed a quick grin, clearly catching the subtle reference to the *Fawlty Towers* "Don't Mention The War" episode. Or perhaps he was simply acknowledging yet another of my quirky, poorly informative bulletins.

Elsbeth's face lit up as John approached. She remembered him. Good. They'd sort Harold out.

Our caterer approached with a tray of baked goodies.

"It must be difficult navigating this crowd," I commented, snatching up the closest shortbread cookie.

"Hey, it's a good thing, Kelly. You wanted it 'packed to the gills,'" she reminded me before moving on.

I bit into the buttery goodness, closed my eyes and soaked up the swirling festive chatter. Napoleon Bonaparte, of all people, said it best. *"Strangers are just friends waiting to happen."*

I glanced around the showroom and a warmth stole over me. I knew almost everyone here and was good friends with many. I wouldn't change a thing. Godfrey caught my pleased expression and raised his glass in a subtle salute. He understood. This was so much more than a business effort to push product. FROG was hosting an extended family Christmas party tonight.

I brushed off the wayward crumbs and headed over to Gerome and Dan.

"Just the gal we wanted to see. Can you tell us the secrets to this marvelous chest, Kelly?"

I most certainly could.

There's More In Store ...

No matter how tired, Francine always found time for journaling. "You never know, Kel, someone might want to write a book about our FROG days."

The first thing I ever bought from FROG, only to have it sold out from under me.

Popular FROG table bases. If phone cameras were a thing in the 80's, I could have shared a photo of the famous actor who went home with a set of penguins.

Yes, the inventory really was stacked to the ceiling at FROG. What emergency exit?

Francine was always a few steps ahead.

Heading back to Kowloon after a successful day of inventory buying.

"The dentist" and "the children's book author" out and about in Hong Kong.

Posing with "Fred," the boss, and a gate guardian on the grounds of the Grand Palace in Bangkok.

God help me if I dropped Francine's infamous leather tote over the side of this Bangkok paddle boat.

Just breathe.

Francine attempted to charm me into ordering a dozen of these frogs from a small factory in Northern Thailand. We bought four. Less was always more.

*The Chiang Mai ceramic factory
where I took one for the team.*

"Does it suit me, Kel?"

*Outside the entrance to
the Temple of the Emerald
Buddha in Bangkok.*

*"We'd be the same height if
I had my shoes on, Kel."*

*Some last-minute prep as we flew
to Korea for the first time.*

*On the home stretch
of the 1986 Vancouver
Marathon.*

Just married.

*A relaxed Francine and her
jade bracelets on the Tolmie
Street deck. It must have been a
good day at FROG.*

*Dining out with the 95-year-old
Francine in Santa Monica in 2017.*

About the Author

Kelly McKenzie worked at her mother's Vancouver Asian antique store for over a decade. After struggling to make her first sale, she went on to become her mother's dependable right-hand gal, picking up bookkeeping skills, marathon running and a husband along the way. A cast member of Seattle's first Listen To Your Mother show, she's been published in community newspapers across Canada, in the Chicken Soup for the Soul book series and in various blogs and anthologies. Never, Never, Hardly Ever is a result of Frankie's endless encouragement to "get our antics out into the world." Follow Kelly's whimsy and antics at kellylmckenzie.com or on Instagram and Facebook @kellylmckenzie

Gratitudes

To our customers who enabled FROG to thrive for seventeen years in Vancouver – thank you. You enriched our lives in ways far beyond the monetary.

To the followers of my *Just TypiKel* blog – thank you for encouraging me to share more of the quirky Francine stories. You gave me the confidence to explore the options beyond a somewhat restrictive 750 word count.

To Liz Cullen and Julie Lingley – thank you for volunteering to critique Chapter One's very first draft. Your feedback nudged me to keep going.

To Katie Clooney of the *Preppy Empty Nester* blog, and to our mutual friend Mo Lux – thank you for your unwavering support. I value our unique friendship. Here's to sharing a "Mo-approved" bottle of wine or two in the near future.

To the inimitable Allia Zobel Nolan – thank you for your expert advice and for introducing me to Jacky. I'm grateful we met at the 2016 Erma Bombeck Writers' Workshop, Allia. May we enjoy many more laughs and slices of cheesecake.

To Mary Marshall – thank you for wading through countless drafts of Chapters One through Eight. I quite understand if you're tempted to just skip right on over to Chapter Nine.

To Chelsea Armstrong – thank you for your insightful notes regarding the early chapters. I always said you could write.

To Asya Blue of Asya Blue Design – thank you for taking on the formatting of the interior of *Never, Never, Hardly Ever*. I truly appreciate your expertise, clever suggestions, and the swift responses to my questions. I am very lucky to have you on the team.

To my project manager – Amanda Miller of My Word Publishing – thank you for your sense of humor, vision and tenacity. It was a joy working with you to bring *Never, Never, Hardly Ever* into the world. Your insightful guidance throughout the entire process – even during the holidays – was above and beyond. Thank you.

To my editor, Jacqueline Smith of Wordsmith – *Never, Never, Hardly Ever* would be a very different book without your efforts. Let's meet in person so I can thank you properly. In the meantime, thank you for reining in my excessive use of adjectives and for being so generous regarding the second sweep of the manuscript.

To Meredith McKenzie – thank you for your quiet support and the not-so-subtle suggestions to seek advice from Henry and Lance.

To Henry McKenzie – bless you for never shying away from manuscript status updates and for ensuring my headshot was anchored.

To Lance Robinson – I apologize for laboring under a misapprehension. As the first to read the manuscript all the way through – the bloated version of over 88,000 words, at that – you are actually my alpha reader. Your keen eye strengthened the story, from my defense of the importance of Billie, to your insistence that I offer the readers "some well-deserved slices of the nuptials cake." If not for you … what wedding? Thank you for your profound positivity and fierce support, dear alpha reader. It means the world to me.

And finally – infinite thanks to Francine for your obsessive journaling. *Never, Never, Hardly Ever* would be just a slim pamphlet without the 1983 - 1993 diaries. Your descriptive details triggered so many memories of our time together at FROG. What a gift. Thank you, Mom, for everything.

Opportunities to Connect

Invite Kelly to Your Book Club!

As a special nod to Never, Never, Hardly Ever readers, Kelly is offering to visit with your book club either virtually or in-person.

She Speaks, Too!

Elevate your podcast with Kelly as a guest! From laughter-inducing ancedotes to profound life lessons, she weaves a narrative that resonates with audiences. When you invite Kelly, expect an episode that promises to be enlightening, entertaining, and full of valuable takeaways.

To schedule an appearance at your book club or next speaking engagement, please contact Kelly directly: kmckenzie13@gmail.com

Before You Go...

Please consider leaving an honest review on Amazon or Goodreads.

Reviews help spread the word and are greatly appreciated by the author.

Made in the USA
Las Vegas, NV
21 March 2024

87467630R00204